STORIES BY KATHRYN JACKSON

THE ANIMALS' MERRY CHRISTMAS

PICTURES BY

RICHARD SCARRY

Golden Press • New York
Western Publishing Company, Inc.
Racine, Wisconsin

CONTENTS

A LITTLE deer came skipping home through the snowy woods. His eyes were still shining from the wonderful things he had seen. His heart felt as light as a snowflake, and as warm as he always felt close to his mother's side.

"Oh, Mother!" he cried. "I went to the town and peeped in the window of a house. There was a tree inside, glittering and shining, with stars caught in its branches—red and green ones, blue and white. And it was all hung with bright balls that sparkled the light all over the room!"

The mother deer nodded her head slowly. Her eyes shone, too.

"That was a Christmas tree," she said softly. "At Christmas time, people deck their trees with lights and toys and shining things—"

"Christmas tree!" whispered the little deer. "Oh, Mother, I want a Christmas tree!"

The mother deer pawed the snowy ground thoughtfully. Oh, how much she wanted a tree for her baby! At last an idea came to her.

"Follow me," she said. She took her baby farther into the woods, and showed him a small green tree in a little clearing.

Christmas Tree

"We'll put berries on the branches. We'll put tasty shoots on them and tender roots."

The little deer helped. He worked busily. But when the tree was dressed, it was not bright and shining like the tree in town.

"Never mind," said his mother. "Wait until morning. Then we'll come to look at it again."

Soon the baby deer was back at home, tucked closely to his mother's side. Soon he was asleep in the dark, snow-clad woods. And just as the sun came up, his mother awakened him.

Deep into the woods they went on their quiet feet. Close to the clearing they stopped and peeped in. The little deer opened his eyes and his mouth. Icicles hung from his Christmas tree, shining with sunrise. Snowflakes sparkled on it, in red and blue and green. And on all the branches were dozens of bright singing birds, eating the berries and roots and shoots.

"Merry Christmas!" they sang on that early Christmas morning. "Merry Christmas!" they chattered between bites.

The little deer nuzzled his nose in his mother's neck.

"It's a beautiful tree!" he whispered. "Much more beautiful than the tree in town!"

And still the birds sang, and the mother deer smiled happily, and one by one, the other animals came through the woods to look at the little deer's wonderful singing Christmas tree.

A Pig's Christmas

A pig went to market,
His heart full of glee,
To buy his friends presents.
"Not ONE thing for me!"
Said he, said he, said the pig.

He saw some red mittens
With green Christmas trees.
"What size?" asked the clerk.
"MY size, if you please!"
Said he, said he, said the pig.

"I'll buy me this sweater,
These boxing gloves, too,
This sled which just suits me!
Some taffy to chew———"
Said he, said he, said the pig.

"A book and some apples
Come next on my list,
And I think I should have
A real watch for my wrist,"
Said he, said he, said the pig.

"They're fine!" said his friends.
"You've bought SO much for you
That we'll get you no presents.
What else can we do?"
Said they, said they, said his friends.

And on Christmas Eve
All under his tree
Were the presents he'd bought.
"Merry Christmas to me!"
Said he, said he, said the pig.

But it wasn't much fun
Giving things to himself.
So he took down his pig bank
That stood on the shelf.
"Let's see, let's see," said the pig.

"I'll go shopping right now,
And I'll spend every dime
To buy my friends presents.
I'm glad there's still time!"
With glee, said he, said that pig.

10

GREEN CHRISTMAS

1. "It's almost Christmas, and still no snow!"
   Cry the woodland creatures. "We still can go
   Out of our houses to search for roots
   And seeds in the dry grass, and maybe shoots
   Of fern and fennel that think it's spring.
   We may find acorns—'most anything
   That's good to eat may be in sight
   For Christmas dinner, on such a night,
   When the ground is bare of ice and snow,
   And stars are bright, and the winds don't blow.
   Hurrah for Christmas and still no snow!"

2. "It's almost Christmas, and still no snow!"
   Sigh the townsfolk, wishing the wind would blow.
   "Our doors are wreathed with pine and holly,
   And our Christmas trees would look extra jolly
   Blazing with lights—if the snow came down
   Deep and white all over the town!
   Why doesn't the sky go woolly gray?
   Why doesn't it snow for Christmas Day?
   It's not like Christmas without some snow!"
   Sigh the townsfolk, wishing the wind would blow—

3.   BUT—
   "Hurrah for Christmas and still no snow!"
   Cry the woodland creatures, and out they go.

11

MR. HEDGEHOG'S CHRISTMAS FEELING

MR. Hedgehog shook Mrs. Hedgehog.

And Mrs. Hedgehog shook all the little hedgehogs.

"What's wrong?" they asked drowsily.

"Yes," asked Mrs. Hedgehog sleepily, "what's wrong?"

Mr. Hedgehog stretched and grinned.

"Nothing's *wrong*," he said. "It's just that I have the best kind of wonderful feeling. It's the kind of feeling that says:

"There's snow all about and the stars are keen,
And the berries are red and the holly is green,
The bells are ringing such joyous carols—
There's mincemeat soaking in spicy barrels,
Puddings are steaming, rich and tasty,
There's many a cake and many a pasty
Rising, or bubbling syrupy juice,
And many a turkey and many a goose
Is roasting brown in a roasting pan.
I simply DON'T believe I can
Sleep in a burrow underground
With so many Christmas joys around!"

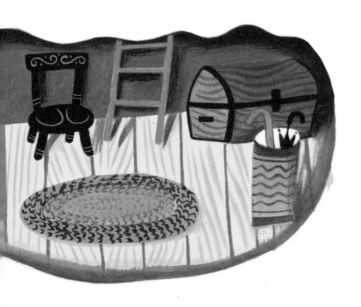

"Very well," smiled Mrs. Hedgehog, merrily shaking moth balls out of her muff.

"Where are we going?" asked the little Hedgehogs. They all reached for their coats.

"To town!" cried Mr. Hedgehog, who had found his Sunday hat. "To London-town!"

He scampered out of the burrow and up the nearest holly tree. There he picked a large sprig of holly for Mrs. Hedgehog's muff, small sprigs for all the little Hedge-hogs' buttonholes, and a very large sprig, bright with berries, to tuck in the band of his own hat.

"Now we are ready to go to London-town," laughed Mr. Hedgehog.

"Ready every one," said Mrs. Hedge-hog.

Then arm in arm, the Hedgehog family hurried through the snowy twilight, head-ing for the lights of Londontown, and the wonderful Christmas sights they would see.

MR. HEDGEHOG'S CHRISTMAS PRESENT

London town was even more wonderful than Mr. Hedgehog had imagined. The stores were a miracle of shining lights and splendid sights!

Even the mice went about with presents for their friends, and "Merry Christmas" on their lips.

"I should like to get a present for Mrs. Hedgehog!" said Mr. Hedgehog to himself.

What should it be?

Not a fur coat. Mrs. Hedgehog had one that suited her perfectly.

Not a diamond tiara. That would be too heavy for her head. Might make it ache!

Surely not a bottle of scent. Hedgehogs like the smell of fern and hawthorne.

Suddenly something lovely caught Mr. Hedgehog's eye. A bright red apple lay in the clean snow near the curb, lost and forgotten!

Mr. Hedgehog picked it up and brushed off the snow. He polished it with his mittens.

Solemnly he offered it to his wife. "A Merry Christmas, my dear!" he said.

Mrs. Hedgehog kissed him. "Thank you," she said. "I'll make us a big, sweet, warm apple dumpling of it!"

The little Hedgehogs, one and all, smacked their lips and shouted "Merry Christmas" again and again.

And arm in arm the Hedgehog family hurried home to their cozy burrow, which soon smelled excitingly of apple and spice and crisp pastry browning—

The very merriest kind of Christmas smell!

The Snowshoe Rabbits

FIVE happy rabbits sat close to the fireplace in their snug little house. One was the mother rabbit, one was the daddy rabbit, and three were young rabbits who had never seen Christmas.

"First of all, there will be the tree," said the mother rabbit. "Grandma always has a Christmas tree. It will be dressed with popcorn and berries, and lighted with candles. And on it there will be presents for three good little rabbits!"

The little rabbits' eyes shone just as if the candles were lighted right then.

"And, of course, your Grandpa will play his rabbit piano," grinned the daddy rabbit. "He'll play 'Jingle Bells' and 'Deck the Halls' and 'The First Noël.'"

Now the little rabbits began to hum.

They knew all those songs. They knew all about Christmas at Grandma's. So they sang till their ears waggled.

Then one little rabbit hopped up. He was a fat little rabbit, licking his lips.

"After that comes Christmas dinner," he said. "A big roast carrot basted with sugar, mashed turnips with butter, and cranberries red and shining. And for dessert, a round pudding all lighted up, with holly on top!"

That fat little rabbit flopped back in his chair.

"I can hardly wait for tomorrow," he whispered. "I can hardly wait to go to Grandma's!"

The other little rabbits nodded very hard.

The mother rabbit smiled.

"We'll go early in the morning," said the daddy rabbit, looking at his watch. "And right now it's time good little rabbits were in bed."

16

17

"We'll never be able to go to Grandma's now!" said his brother.

And the little girl rabbit pulled her apron over her head to hide her tears.

By and by the three little rabbits crept downstairs. Sorry little rabbits they were, full of gulps and sighs and tears that almost spilled over.

Their mother and daddy didn't seem sad at all. They talked happily all through breakfast, just as if nothing had happened. After breakfast their daddy hurried up to the attic. Back he came, smiling and proud, with some queer-looking things under his arm. They looked like tennis rackets. But who plays tennis in the deep snow?

Nobody.

In the whisk of a whisker all three little rabbits were in their beds and sound asleep.

They dreamed of shining candles
And wonderful presents
And beautiful smells
And a glossy tree
And a sprinkling of snow.

But when they hopped out of bed in the morning and looked out the window, there was no sprinkling of snow.

Sprinkling, indeed!

It had snowed all through the night. Snow covered the hills and the long grass and all the rabbit paths. It was heaped halfway up the house, deeper than boots, deeper than leggings—deeper than the three little rabbits themselves!

"It's too deep!" whispered the fat little rabbit.

"What *are* they?" asked the fat little rabbit at last.

"Snowshoes," laughed the daddy rabbit. "They're for walking right on top of deep snow."

None of the little rabbits waited to hear any more. They scrambled into their warmest clothes. They gathered up all the exciting, secret present packages they had made.

And before very long, out into the crisp white snow went the whole rabbit family. Across the deep snow they tramped in those wonderful snowshoes.

They made big scuffy tracks from their house straight toward their Grandma's house.

And as they went they sang:

Snowshoe rabbits in the snow,
Off to Grandma's house we go—
Holly, pudding, popcorn, toys,
Shining candles, lots of noise;
Off to Grandma's house we go!
Sing for Christmas!
Sing for snow!

MOUSE CHRISTMAS

Oh, the wonderful bits
That folks drop as they go,
Cooking and baking
And hurrying so!
Citron and raisins
And powdery spice,
Sugar and currants—
It's nice to be mice

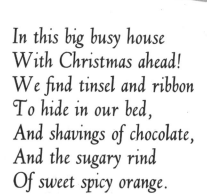

In this big busy house
With Christmas ahead!
We find tinsel and ribbon
To hide in our bed,
And shavings of chocolate,
And the sugary rind
Of sweet spicy orange.

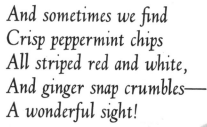

And sometimes we find
Crisp peppermint chips
All striped red and white,
And ginger snap crumbles—
A wonderful sight!

We'll fill up our stockings,
When Christmas Eve comes,
With the savory bits
And the wonderful crumbs;
Citron and raisins
And sugar and spice—
Oh, just before Christmas
It's NICE to be mice!

20

A VERY SMALL CHRISTMAS

I wonder if the chipmunks know,
When everything is white with snow
And night starts coming very fast,
That Christmas time is here at last?

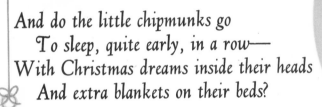

And do the little chipmunks go
To sleep, quite early, in a row—
With Christmas dreams inside their heads
And extra blankets on their beds?

And do they hop up just at dawn
And put their robes and slippers on
And hurry out to peep and see
If someone brought a Christmas tree?

If someone did, I wonder who?
Their chimney's small to wriggle through!
Their Christmas tree must be a twig—
But maybe chipmunks think it's big.
I hope it's trimmed with sunflower seeds,
And peanuts, too, and icy beads,
And lighted candles (birthday size)
To make a grand chipmunk surprise!

TERRIBLE TEDDY BEAR

NOW Terrible Teddy Bear did not look like a terrible bear at all. He was the brown kind of teddy bear, just the size to take to bed. And he had a funny little squeak, and shiny black eyes and a bit of a smile. But he WAS a terrible teddy just the same.

Even Santa Claus, who had made this teddy and who had said, "He's the best bear I ever did make!" decided that at last.

"This terrible teddy bear!" he said the first Christmas morning at breakfast. "This terrible teddy bear climbed out of my pack last night. He hid under the seat of my sleigh. When I got back home, there he was—back home too! And not where-ever I meant to leave him for some good child!"

"Dear, dear!" said Mrs. Santa Claus.

And she was still saying "Dear, dear!" five Christmases later. Because every Christmas Eve, Terrible Teddy Bear climbed out of the toy pack. Every Christ-

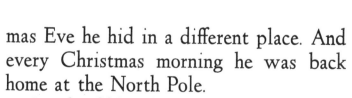

mas Eve he hid in a different place. And every Christmas morning he was back home at the North Pole.

On the fifth Christmas morning Santa Claus made up his mind to do something about Terrible Teddy.

He hurried into his workshop and looked at the letters in the basket marked NO! That basket was chockful of letters from people who didn't deserve presents and did not get presents. Santa Claus al-

22

ways felt very sad when he looked at those letters.

Just the same, he sat down and read them all.

He read straight through lunch and halfway through supper. Then he jumped up, holding a crumpled letter in one red mitten.

"Here is a letter from someone more terrible than Terrible Teddy," he said. "Here is a letter from Terrible Tommy, who says 'I won't' all day long, and eats nothing but candy and bubble gum, and besides—he never will go to bed at night."

"Dear, dear!" said Mrs. Santa Claus. "You can't EVER take him a present!"

"Oh, yes I can," Santa laughed. "I'm going to his house right now—a special trip. And I'm going to give him Terrible Teddy!"

"Dear, dear!" Mrs. Santa Claus said. "Dear, dear, dear, dear, dear, dear, dear, dear!"

But by that time the reindeer were harnessed, the sleigh was out of the barn. And Santa was driving over the roof tops on Christmas night.

He was driving one-handed at that. In his other hand he held Terrible Teddy, tight as tight.

Terrible Teddy certainly didn't look terrible now. He was trying very hard to squeak, "Oh, please don't give me to Terrible Tommy!" But Santa held him too tightly.

23

Before long the sleigh stopped with a jerk. It stopped on the roof of Tommy's house.

All the lights were out.

Everyone was asleep. Everyone, that is, except Terrible Tommy.

He sat by the hearth, rubbing his eyes and blowing his nose. He sobbed a bit, too.

"Santa Claus didn't come to me," he cried. "He didn't bring me a thing. Not even some ashes and switches. Not even some old, worn, patched britches. Not even a horn that wouldn't blow. Not even anything. Oh, oh, oh! And I wanted a teddy bear, even an old one, a brown and plushy and nice-to-hold one—with shiny eyes in his fuzzy head, the kind that's the size for taking to bed."

Santa Claus, up on the roof, heard Terrible Tommy. He blew some ashes down to make Tommy close his eyes. And when Tommy did—

Whisk! down the chimney came Santa.

Whisk! up he went again, leaving Terrible Teddy behind.

Away went the sleigh with its bells all jingling.

Terrible Tommy opened his eyes—and there, right in front of him, sat Terrible Teddy.

"Santa did come!" cried Tommy. "He made a special trip just for me—and he brought the nicest, softest, best kind of Teddy Bear in the whole world!"

24

He picked up Terrible Teddy and hugged him tightly. Teddy liked that so much that he hugged back. Tommy liked *that* so much that he felt good from head to toe.

And right then all the Terrible went straight out of Tommy.

It went out of Teddy, too.

Up the stairs they went, both together. Both together they climbed into Tommy's bed. Both together they went sound asleep.

And they looked just like a good little boy sleeping, and a good teddy bear sleeping, too.

By that time, of course, Santa Claus was back at the North Pole.

"Dear, dear, dear," said Mrs. Santa. "I just don't think you should have gone on that special trip. I just don't think you should have taken a present to anyone who is bad!"

Santa Claus chuckled and hung up his hat. He laughed and hung up his coat.

"I'll tell you a secret, Mrs. Santa," he said. "Terrible Tommy isn't bad any more. He's as good as a boy can be. Terrible Teddy isn't bad, either."

Then Santa Claus clapped his knees with pleasure.

"I always did say he was the best bear I ever made," he said. "And it wouldn't be right for Santa Claus to be wrong, would it, now?"

Mrs. Santa Claus didn't say "Dear, dear!"

She said:
"Of course not.
That would
Never
Never
NEVER
Do!"

MR. LION'S PLUM PUDDING

MLION read his letter over and over.
"Well, well," he declared at last,
"that's the finest thing I ever heard."
"What is?" asked Mrs. Lion.
"My cousin Barnaby,—you remember

him, my dear? He was, er, captured and
kindly consented to go to America to live
in a zoo. Well, my dear, he says here that
in America they have Christmas. Sounds
like a most wonderful kind of day, full of
presents and snow and candles and candies
and cookies. And probably the best part
of all is the last, which is called plum pudding!"

"What won't they think of next?"
said Mrs. Lion in a sort of faraway voice,
because she was busily cleaning the
kitchen.

"Hmmm," grunted Mr. Lion, reading
his letter just once more. Then he folded
it neatly, put it on the shelf, and rubbed
his chin.

"Mrs. Lion," he said. "Mrs. Lion, we
are going to have Christmas!"

"But I'm just finishing spring house cleaning!" cried Mrs. Lion.

"Never mind that," her husband said, and he began at once to make his plans for Christmas.

"Snow we can't have," he decided. "Presents are out, because I spent my allowance on a beaver hat. Candles and candies and cookies sound lovely, except that I don't know what they are. But plum pudding—now, plum pudding we shall have!"

He opened the cupboards and pulled out bowls. He went to the flour bin and measured flour, spilling it in drifts from one end of the kitchen to the other.

Mrs. Lion grumbled, but Mr. Lion only laughed. "Looks like snow," he said. "Leave it there!"

He stewed plums with sugar until they boiled all over the stove. Then he chopped a bowl of nuts so vigorously that they bounced about the house like popcorn.

"Oh, dear!" sighed Mrs. Lion. "Oh, dear."

"Now for the suet!" cried Mr. Lion.

He took a large chunk from the refrigerator and mixed it with the other good things. He added more sugar and pinches of spice, and handfuls of raisins; and he worked the whole thing into a round, sticky, slippery ball with his paws. That looked like such fun that Mrs. Lion had to try it, too.

She reached for the pudding, and it slid out of Mr. Lion's paws and out of her paws. Mr. Lion's plum pudding rolled round and round the kitchen, picking up sugar and nuts and flour and raisins as it went.

At last it stopped in the corner.

"Looks ready to cook," grinned Mr. Lion. He wrapped the pudding in one of his wife's best napkins, and since he had to go to the linen closet for that, there were floury tracks all through the house.

27

But before long, Mr. Lion's pudding was steaming. Before long, Mr. and Mrs. Lion's house smelled richly of spices and plums and sugar. Several friends, Mr. and Mrs. Camel, Grandfather Bear, and Trump, the youngest elephant, dropped in unexpectedly.

"How nice to see you!" cried Mr. Lion. "How did you happen to come?"

"Just followed our noses," grinned Trump, and his long nose certainly was pointing straight at the pudding.

"The pudding!" Mrs. Lion said. "I do believe it's done!"

She put it on the table, roly-poly and steaming and set about with juicy raisins and plums. Mr. Lion stuck a red flower in the center to serve as holly, and everyone sat down to eat.

"A Merry Christmas to all!" cried Mr. Lion.

All his friends bowed and said Merry Christmas, too. And that plum pudding was so delicious that even Mrs. Lion forgot the fuss and bother it had made in her spring-cleaned house.

She did say later, "Nice as Christmas is, Mrs. Camel, I'm glad it comes only once a year!"

"Not here!" said her husband. "No, indeed. I'm going to find out all about candles and candies and cookies from Barnaby—and THEN we'll have Christmas once every month, at the very least!"

S U R P R I S E !

The pony was green.
(It's as true as can be!)
The camel was purple.
(A strange sight to see!)
A sugar-white panther
Who looked rather pale
Was resting his paws
On a blue monkey's tail.
The lion was yellow,
As fierce as can be—
"I'll eat you all up
In a one-two-and-three!"
He growled at the others.
But quicker than scat
Somebody said, "Cookies!
And frosted at that!"
Somebody said, "Yummy!"
And reached out a hand
And gobbled the lion,
Who tasted just grand.
He was gone in a wink
(Which is half of a look)
And NOBODY missed him—
Not even the cook!

THE GOAT WHO PLAYED SANTA CLAUS

NCE upon a time there were five little chicks who thought Santa Claus was sure to come to them. It was the day before Christmas, and they were very much excited.

"He'll bring us a tree of the Christmas kind," they told each other. "And five Christmas presents—one for each!"

Everyone in the barnyard wanted those chicks to have a happy Christmas.

But Grandmother Goose was worried.

And old Turkey Gobbler was very worried.

"Santa Claus never *did* come to us," he said. "I just don't think he comes to barnyards."

"Neither do I," sighed Grandmother Goose. "And what I say is, somebody should *tell* those chicks."

She tied on her shawl.

Old Turkey Gobbler pulled on his cap.

"Come along," he said. "We'll tell them."

But before they had gone two waddles and a strut, fat Uncle Pig hurried up to them.

"Oh no, you don't," he cried. "You're not going to spoil those little chicks' fun!"

The cow agreed.

So did the horse.

"Indeed you won't!" bleated the sheep, running up.

Mother Hen smiled.

"Good!" she cackled. "I just do want my chicks to have a nice Christmas!"

Old Turkey Gobbler snorted.

"All very well," he said. "But what about Christmas morning?"

"What about when they find that Santa *didn't* come?" asked Grandmother Goose.

"Oh," said Mother Hen.

She looked sadly at her yellow chicks, who were skittering around trying to sing "Up on the Housetop" in their peeping voices. She looked even more sadly at her barnyard friends.

"My chicks were so sure Santa Claus would come," she sighed, "that I myself was believing it, too."

The cow and the horse and the sheep sighed deeply.

Grandmother Goose started toward the happy chicks.

But fat Uncle Pig had a sudden and wonderful idea.

He saw the white goat strolling up and down near the clothesline, his snowy beard wagging merrily. He saw the clothes flapping on the line. There were red mittens drying, and a fine suit of the farmer's red underwear. There was a pillow case blowing out, just as if it were a pack full of presents for five little chicks.

"I have a feeling that Santa Claus is really coming to those chicks!" Uncle Pig squealed. "Just you wait and see!"

Then he whispered his wonderful idea to the other animals. Mother Hen was so pleased that she ran in circles until she saw everything twice. The cow and the horse grinned from ear to ear.

"Maybe the goat won't help," sighed Grandmother Goose.

"I'll ask him," smiled the sheep. And she went and talked to the goat.

His eyes twinkled.

"I'd love to do it," he said. "Sounds like fun."

The horse, meanwhile, neatly nipped the clothespins from the red mittens, the red underwear, and the pillowcase, and took them off the line.

Uncle Pig, meanwhile, went looking in the junk heap in back of the barn. He looked very sharply, and what did he find?

Oh, some wonderful things: a small tin bank made like a drum, a little red wagon missing one wheel, a small red mitten with a hole in the thumb, a bright green sock that had no mate, a pair of doll's skates (thrown away by mistake), and bits of spruce branches, too small to use in the farmhouse.

"What else do I need?" he said to himself.

Pussycat Smart came padding up.

"Me," she said. "You need me to help tie those bits into a tree. You need me to fix the little wagon with a new wheel, and to pin up the small mitten's hole in the thumb. And you need me to get some crabapples out of the barrel. We'll hang them on the tree!"

The two worked together.

By the time it was late afternoon, they had made a splendid little tree, and Pussycat Smart had put a new wheel on the wagon.

Then they looked at the presents.

"Rather dirty," mewed Pussycat Smart. "They need a good scrub!"

She ran to fetch Grandmother Goose.

"You're the only one of us who can wash them," she mewed.

Grandmother Goose started to say, "Oh, I'm afraid I can't get them clean!" But just then she saw the fine little Christmas tree.

And just then the white goat came around the barn. He made such a jolly Santa Claus all dressed in the red underwear suit, with the red mittens on his ears for a cap and the pillow case slung over his shoulder, that she laughed.

"I'll polish them spic and span!" she promised.

She washed the presents until they looked like new.

Not to be outdone, old Turkey Gobbler filled the drum and wagon and the one red mitten and the one green sock with chicken corn.

Now everything was ready.

Pretty soon the dusk was dark.

33

Pretty soon the lights in the farmhouse went out.

Pretty soon the stars were shining, and the five little chicks were fast asleep in the chicken coop.

"It's time to go," whispered the barnyard animals. "Come on, Santa Claus goat!"

"I still have things to do," laughed the goat. "Besides, Santa Claus never comes until everyone is asleep."

"That's right!" all the animals agreed, and they hurried away to their beds. All of them were so glad that Santa Claus was coming to the chicks! But all of them had a wish they were wishing, too.

It was Grandmother Goose who said the wish right out loud.

"I wish Santa Claus would come to me just once," she said, and then she fell asleep.

The Santa Claus goat finished doing the things he still had to do. When he started out, his pack was jammed-crammed full. There seemed to be so much more in it than presents for five little chicks.

34

Then he tiptoed into the barn and put down his pack.

Out of it he took presents and presents and presents for everyone in the barn.

"A new shawl for Grandmother Goose," he chuckled. "And a basket of apples for the horse. Turnips for the sheep, corn for old Turkey Gobbler, a good smoking pipe for fat Uncle Pig, a catnip mouse for Pussycat Smart, and a bell for Cow. For good Mother Hen, a new blue bonnet——and for me, a rich plum pudding to eat, can and all!"

Very tired he was, the Santa Claus goat, from collecting all those splendid presents. But now the barn looked as exciting as a Christmas tree. He could hardly wait for morning!

"Sleeping's the very best way to get morning to come," the Santa Claus goat told himself wisely.

And he crept quietly into his bed and was soon asleep, still dressed in his funny red Santa Claus suit, and still feeling warm and merry inside from being such a wonderful make-believe Santa Claus.

35

THE GOLDEN SLED

ONCE upon a time, when Christmas was coming, there was a little brown bear who wanted a sled very much. He started to write a letter to Santa Claus, and then he began to wonder what color sled he wanted.

"Let's see," said this little bear. "Let me see. . . . Some bears like red things best. But I'm not that kind of bear. Some bears like blue things. But I'm not that kind of bear, either."

He remembered hearing about a little bear who wanted his whole room painted purple.

"Purple, purple, purple everywhere!" said the little brown bear. "Now I wouldn't like that at all!"

And he began to look all around the dining room, to see what color he liked best. There was a tall white chocolate pot with golden flowers on it. Those flowers were wonderfully shiny! There was a black chair with golden squiggles on the back. It was a gay chair, very nice for rocking oneself. And the little bear thought the golden squiggles made it even nicer.

There was a golden clock that ticked merrily—tickety-tock, tockety-tick. And there was a fat round jar with letters on it.

The letters were golden.

They spelled out H-O-N-E-Y.

"Honey!" laughed the little bear. "Golden letters spell honey, and honey is golden—and golden gold is the color I like best!"

So he put that in his letter.

"PLEAZ BRING ME A GOLDEN SLED."

"A golden sled!" said his mother when she saw the letter. "Oh, my! You'll have to be a very good bear to get a *golden* sled!"

"Yes, indeed," said his father. "You'll have to be just as good as gold!"

"Well, I just will!" the little bear said. "I'll just be the very best bear ever."

He brushed his fur suit until it was fluffy and shiny, put on his warm fur cap, and hurried out to mail his letter.

"Oh, my!" said Santa Claus when he read the letter. "A *golden* sled! Well, here's a problem for me! Golden paint is the hardest to get. Golden paint is what I have the least of! And here's a little bear that wants a whole sled painted golden!"

He thought about that while he was making the sled, and he shook his head.

When the sled was all finished (except for paint), Santa Claus looked at his little jar of golden paint.

"It would take every last drop to paint this sled," he said. "I wouldn't have one smidgeon left to put on anybody's engine, or anybody's chair, or anybody's doll-baby's locket!"

And then Santa Claus decided he would have a look at this good little bear who wanted a golden sled.

So he whizzed up his chimney, climbed out on his roof, and sat down. He took out his spy-glass, and pointed it at the little bear's house. He turned it a bit this way, and a bit that way, to see better.

Now Santa Claus could see the little bear. And oh, my! he could hardly believe his eyes!

First he saw the little bear making his own bed, neat and tidy, tight as a drum.

Then he saw the little bear eating his breakfast, good as gold, with a yum-yum-yum.

He saw the little bear drying the dishes
And putting them away
And sweeping the porch
And putting all the rubber boots in a row, easy to find.

Santa Claus saw the little bear going to the store with a long list, and not forgetting anything.

He saw that little bear helping old bears across the street
And minding baby bears for their mothers
And saying "yes, ma'am" and "no, sir" with the kindest and most friendly of smiles.

And all this time Santa Claus could see the little bear's good little heart shining right through his furry coat! It was dancing a happy dance, thumpity-thump—and it was a shining heart, golden as golden, because the little bear was SO good.

"Well, I declare," cried Santa Claus. "This little bear, this good little bear who wants a golden sled, has a heart of gold!"

That made Santa Claus think twice.

He whizzed down his chimney and took his little jar of golden paint in one hand. Then he searched in his paint box, and way down at the bottom he found a little jar of silver paint, too.

"That does it!" he grinned. "I can put silver on all the engines, instead of gold. I can put silver on all the chairs. And this year, everybody's doll baby will have a silver locket instead of a golden one!"

Humming to himself, Santa Claus dipped a brush into the golden paint and began to paint the little bear's sled. When the little jar of paint was empty, with not a smidgeon of paint left, the sled was all painted shiny, bright, glittering, glistening, sparkling gold!

And when the good little bear woke up on Christmas morning and put on his slippers and scampered downstairs—

There was his sled under the tree—
Golden as golden!

"Oh, lovely!" he whispered. "And I never did think I'd get a whole golden sled. I never did think I could be good enough!"

His mother kissed him and said, "Why, you're the best little bear in the whole world!"

His father patted his head and said, "Yes, sir, you're just as good as gold!"

The little brown bear said "Merry Christmas" to his father and mother.

He put on his mittens and cap and boots.

He took his shining golden sled out into the snowy Christmas day.

And he went coasting down the white hill.

Past the dark green trees
Thinking—
"A great big, bright and golden Merry Christmas to everybody in every place in this whole big shining world!"

THE SECRET RIDE

IT was very late on Christmas night. The barn was dark, and most of the animals were asleep. But not the new Christmas pony. He peeped out at the house. The house was dark, too, and everyone in it was asleep.

The pony turned his glossy head and looked proudly at the new red Christmas sleigh.

His eyes shone, just looking at it.

How fast he had pulled that sleigh all day! How the bells had jingled, and how the children had laughed and shouted and sung! What fun it had been trotting swiftly through the snow with that splendid sleigh!

The pony had wished he could go on and on around the farm, over the hill, across the frozen brook, forever.

"I wish I could go out right now," he thought. "I'd like to see how it feels in the dark with the stars shining and the icy trees glistening, and the wind still and the snow crisp and dry."

He shook his small head impatiently. He winked one eye gaily. And he looked merrily at the lamb and the ducks, the pigs and the calf, the drowsy hens and the brave little rooster.

"Why not?" he asked himself. "Why not take *them* for a ride in the Christmas sleigh?"

40

He nudged the rooster and whispered, "Want to go for a sleigh ride?"

In one second the rooster was wide awake.

"Oh, yes!" he cried.

He crowed a loud crow that awakened all the others. In two seconds they had climbed and scrambled and flapped and clambered into the shiny red sleigh.

"Here we go!" the pigs squealed.

"Merry Christmas!" bleated the lamb.

The hens chuckled and the rooster crowed.

But the Christmas pony said "Oh!" in a surprised way.

"How am I to hitch myself to the sleigh?" he asked. "I don't know how!"

"Oh!" cried the other animals. "Oh, *sad* Christmas! What a disappointment!"

And then Pussycat Smart came padding up.

"I know how," she purred. "I'll do the hitching if I can do the driving."

Nobody argued the least bit about that. And before long, Pussycat Smart had the Christmas sleigh hitched to the Christmas pony. She had the barn doors open, and she sat in the sleigh, holding the reins.

Five little mice came whisking out of the hay.

"We want to go, too!" they squeaked.

42

For a moment Pussycat Smart licked her whiskers. "Oh, yes, my dears," she thought greedily. "You're welcome to go—inside me!"

But after all, it *was* Christmas.

After all, she was quite stuffed with tasty scraps from the table.

"Come along, then," she mewed, slapping the reins until the bells tinkled like hundreds of stars tumbling out of the sky. "Come along, then, you five."

The mice found seats in the folds of the warm fur rug.

The pony pranced lightly across the barn floor.

Then out of the barn went that happy, jingling sleighful of animals. Over the snow they raced, squeaking and bleating, mooing and crowing, cackling and squeaking for joy.

All around the farm they went, in a big zig-zagging line, under the stars, under the glistening trees. They sped across the frozen brook six times for the sport of skidding on the ice. And they went singing up and down the hill.

At last, with their noses and beaks and bills red with cold, they came back to the snug barn.

Pussycat Smart unharnessed the Christmas pony and locked the barn door. The lamb rubbed the snowflakes off the Christmas sleigh. The calf licked the runners dry and shining. The hens folded the warm fur rug, taking orders from the rooster. And the five little mice scurried to bed.

Soon all the animals were in bed, warm and sleepy and happy.

"Everything's tidy," whispered the Christmas pony. "Everything's back in place. Nobody ever will know that I took all the animals for a secret ride on Christmas night."

But that sleepy little pony quite forgot all the extra tracks he had made in the crisp white snow.

Surely the children would see them!

Surely they would wonder about those wild zig-zagging tracks!

Surely they would guess all about that secret ride on Christmas night—and love the new Christmas pony even more for giving a wonderful sleigh ride to all his new friends in the friendly barn!

THE COLD LITTLE SQUIRREL

1 Once there was a little squirrel who was cold—morning, noon, and night—all winter long.

2 But at night he was coldest. And on Christmas Eve, br–r–r! he could not sleep.

3 Out of his house he crept. He sat on a snowy branch, shivering under the stars.

4 "Colder than ever," he said. "But it seems sort of magic, too." Down the tree he ran.

44

5 He scampered across the snow. "Maybe I'll find a warm magic coat," he said. "Maybe, warm boots."

6 Not a thing did he find on that still, magic night. But suddenly he saw something far away.

7 It was a small, cozy house, its windows bright with candles.

The little squirrel ran to it and climbed up on the chimney.

8 Close to the hearth sat a fluffy little raccoon. She was saying to her mother, "I wish Santa would bring me a real live doll!"

9 And just at that moment the cold little squirrel slipped on the ice. Right down the chimney he tumbled!

10 The little raccoon picked him up and hugged him.

"Here's my real live doll!" she cried. "I'll make him a warm little coat and warm boots!"

11 And the cold little squirrel curled up in her arms, cozy and warm on that cold, still, magic night.

THE BARE POLAR BEAR

OW once upon a time there was a big, white, fluffy polar bear who wanted very much to be one of Santa Claus's helpers. Time after time, he knocked on the workshop door and asked if he couldn't please do something to help.

But time after time, the answer he got was no, and thank you most kindly just the same.

The helpers all agreed he was MUCH too big to be a helper. Mrs. Santa Claus said it wouldn't do at all. And Santa himself was too busy to even look up from his work.

At last, only three days before Christmas, the big, white, fluffy polar bear gave up trying. "I'll never get to be a helper," he told himself. "It's no use trying!"

And strangely enough, at that very same moment, Santa Claus was saying "It's no use trying," too!

"There are hundreds of stores where I'm supposed to say hello to the children," he told Mrs. Santa, "and hundreds and hundreds of corners where I'm supposed to ring bells. And the toys aren't quite finished. And besides, there are so many good children this year that I have more chimneys to slide down than ever before!"

Santa Claus said he simply could NOT be everywhere at once. He said it was no use trying.

Mrs. Santa Claus thought very hard.

"Your helpers will be glad to go to the stores and ring the bells for you," she said. "I'll fit them all out in your old Santa Claus suits!"

Everybody heard it.

And especially a big white fluffy polar bear heard it.

He ran straight to the workshop and knocked on the door. Mrs. Santa Claus opened the door and in he went, white and fluffy, sparkling with snow.

"Anything I can do to help?" he asked.

Everyone looked at his fluffy white fur.

"Beards!" whispered Mrs. Santa Claus.

"Wonderful beards!" chuckled Santa himself.

The helpers told the bear their troubles.

"And please, Mr. Bear," they asked. "May we snip off some of your fluffy white fur for beards?"

The bear bowed. "To be sure!" he said.

Up to the attic she ran. In a twinkling, she had the helpers all dressed up in fine, red suits, with pillows for round, jolly tummies.

At first Santa Claus thought they looked splendid.

Then he thought there was something missing.

"Beards!" he cried at last. "They have no beards!"

"Oh, dear!" sighed Mrs. Santa. "They can't go without beards, and there's no time to grow beards. And I have no old Santa Claus beards in the attic, because *you've* always had such a beautiful beard growing right out of your chin!"

"Oh, oh, oh, what are we to do?" cried all the helpers, so sadly that the sound went up the chimney and echoed from iceberg to iceberg all over the North Pole.

Mrs. Santa Claus took her scissors. She snipped here and there while the polar bear stood very still.

"More!" cried the helpers, busily making beards.

More!

More!

More!

Snip! Snip! Snip! went the scissors.

Stitch! Stitch! Stitch! went the helpers.

Before long there were enough fluffy white beards for every single helper.

BUT—

"G–g–g–gracious!" shivered the polar bear. "Don't you think it's turning c–c–c–cold?"

Everyone looked at that nice fluffy polar bear. He wasn't one bit fluffy now. He hadn't a snippet of warm white fur left. All his fur had gone for beards. And he

was shivering and shaking just like the very bare bear he was!

He looked so funny that even Santa wanted to laugh.

"But it's no laughing matter!" he told himself. "This bear will get sniffles without his fur!"

"Couldn't you just sit here by the fire till your fur grows again, Mr. Bear?" asked one helper.

The polar bear looked at his bare paw.

"Well," he sighed. "I did want to go about singing carols. I'm known for my voice, you know. And I did so want to get a Christmas tree for my three little bears. And I'm sure Mrs. Polar Bear would hate me to miss Christmas dinner."

Big tears came to his eyes.

The helpers pulled off their beards and said, "We'll glue your fur back on!"

49

The helpers put on their beards and hurried off to say hello to the children in the stores and to ring bells on corners.

Mrs. Santa baked a big round coffee cake with raisins and icing, and put on a pot of coffee.

And after supper, Santa Claus finished Susie Hopkins' new doll.

"Time for bed!" said Mrs. Santa.

Santa Claus yawned, but he shook his head.

"I'm making three little stuffed polar bears that squeak," he said, picking up bits of polar bear fur. "They're for Mr. Bear's three little boys."

"I do declare you *are* a saint!" smiled Mrs. Santa Claus proudly.

And she sat down beside her husband to make three little red snow suits with zippers for the three little stuffed polar bears that Santa Claus was making for a Christmas surprise.

But at that very moment Mrs. Santa Claus came hurrying up with a measuring tape.

She measured the polar bear.

She cut up a very large piece of red flannel.

She sewed on her whirring sewing machine.

And she put a zipper in what she was making.

When what she was making was made, she helped the polar bear to try it on. It was a most wonderful warm red snow suit, just the right size for the bear. He zipped the zipper, and drew up the hood—and there was that polar bear all cozy and warm again.

He jumped in the air and clicked his heels together. He kissed Mrs. Santa and shook hands with the helpers. He waved to Santa Claus and away he went, eager to show Mrs. Polar Bear his fine new suit.

THE GOOSE THAT STUFFED HERSELF

OW Tobias Tiger was extremely fond of his family. Nothing pleased him so much as to fetch home a surprise

be it a bag of molasses taffy—
or a bit of gay ribbon—
or a fine, juicy soup bone.

A surprise of any kind, tucked in his vest pocket, hidden under his jacket, or slipped up his sleeve, made him grin from one striped ear straight across to the other.

So with Tobias Tiger.

And when he came home, early one gray evening halfway between Thanksgiving and Christmas, with a rather scrawny gray goose—well! you'd have thought that Tobias had fetched home the moon.

He flopped the gray goose, quite limp

with struggling, on the kitchen table and rocked proudly back on his heels.

"Poor thing!" cried Mrs. Tiger (whose name was Tabitha), eying the goose. "Poor thing! It does look cold!"

She wrapped it warmly in her own red shawl and rocked it a bit in her Boston rocker.

The little boy tigers patted its sides.

"A very thin goose, isn't it, Papa?" they asked.

Tobias Tiger tried not to look cross.

"Cold it may be, thin it may be," he said, unwrapping his muffler. "But we'll fatten it up and roast it to a turn—and a splendid dinner it will make us on Christmas day."

Mrs. Tiger stopped rocking the goose.

"What a dandy surprise, Mr. Tiger!" she cried. And she plumped the goose onto

51

Then she flapped happily into Mrs. Tiger's lap, tucked her head under the red shawl, and snored loudly.

Mrs. Tiger rocked her gently. The little boy tigers talked in whispers. And Tobias Tiger (ready for bed in his striped pajamas) said good night in a sort of snort and went upstairs.

Before many days had passed, that goose had made herself one of the family.

She followed Roger Tiger about as if she were a dog. She slept on the foot of Will Tiger's bed. She watched the pots and kettles for Mrs. Tiger. And the minute dinner was ready, she honked a happy honk that was better than a gong or bell.

"I do think she should be allowed to eat with us," whispered Mrs. Tiger. "She could sit in Will's old high chair."

Tobias Tiger put his foot down.

"Indeed she'll not!" he shouted. "She'll eat corn meal behind the stove like a fattening Christmas goose!"

Eat corn meal she did. And by the time Christmas was only a week away, that goose was the plumpest, waddlingest,

most mouth-watering goose in the whole white winter world. Tobias Tiger, who was hiding surprises every night now, thought she was the best surprise he had ever brought home.

her largest platter to see how it would look.

"With a garnish of parsley—" said Tobias Tiger.

"And plenty of stuffing," said his striped sons, "it will make as pretty a goose as ever was eaten!"

At that the goose flipped herself over and began to lick the platter hungrily.

"Can't begin fattening her too soon," Mrs. Tiger observed. She mixed corn meal with milk and stirred it over the fire.

The goose began to eat.

She ate until she was happy.

She ate until she was warm.

She ate until she could not keep one eye open, let alone two.

Roger and Will and Mrs. Tiger thought so, too. But not in quite the same way.

"I've made her a warm red cape and bonnet for Christmas," whispered Mrs. Tiger.

Will said he had made her a wooden eating bowl. And Roger had drawn her a picture of herself, very like her, on a long piece of paper to make room for her neck.

But Tobias Tiger's only concern was how to stuff the Christmas Goose.

"Chestnuts," he decided one night in bed.

The next night he thought, no, bread and celery.

"But I do like a bit of onion," he muttered the following night. Chestnuts and bread and celery and onion swam about in his head.

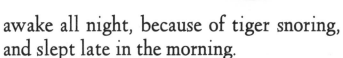

"I can't sleep!" he cried, throwing his pillow on the floor.

Mrs. Tiger brought him another.

"No better!" he shouted.

Roger brought his fluffy pillow and Will brought his puffy pillow.

"No good," sighed Tobias, wide awake. He would still be awake no doubt, except that the goose slipped through the dark and snuggled under his head. She was awake all night, because of tiger snoring, and slept late in the morning.

Tobias was up at dawn.

"This morning," he told his family, "I shall kill the fatted goose."

A small moan escaped Mrs. Tiger.

Roger and Will hid their faces in their paws. And Tobias went searching for the goose. He looked everywhere for her, save, of course, in his bed. By ten o'clock, he was tired out with searching, calling, and roaring.

Up to bed he went.

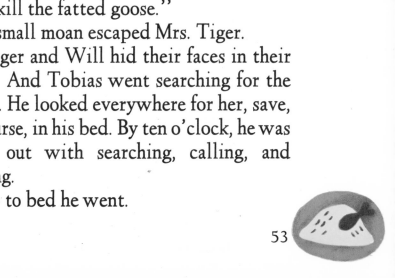

Down he lay. "Lovely, warm, soft pillow," he murmured. "Wouldn't be without it."

Just then the goose stirred and flapped her wings sleepily.

Tobias Tiger leaped out of bed.

"It's you!" he shouted. "It was you all the time!"

The goose smiled sweetly, nodded her head, and went back to her dreams.

"Please don't call our goose 'you,' Papa," whispered Will. "We've named her Tabitha Two, after Mama."

Mrs. Tiger smiled shyly.

And Tobias put on his boots and muffler. Out he went, looking for a surprise. Back he came, with a whopping big turkey all stuffed with chestnuts and bread and celery and onions, and roasted to a turn.

"There," he said proudly. "There's your Christmas dinner. I hope you think it's a good surprise."

"We do," cried Roger and Will and Mrs. Tabitha Tiger all together, hugging him from every side.

Tabitha Two made a noise that sounded like "A superlatively lovely good surprise!"

And on Christmas day she sat at the table in Will's old high chair. She wore her red cape and bonnet. She ate from her new wooden bowl; and she stuffed herself with turkey until she was twice as plump and smiling as the picture Roger had done of her for a special Christmas surprise.

54

A VERY BIG CHRISTMAS

TRUMPET

was a big, friendly elephant who lived all alone in a small zoo. He loved all the children who came to see him, and he listened to everything they said to each other.

So Trumpet knew that boys play marbles in the springtime, and girls jump rope. He knew about picnics and swimming in the summer. He knew all about raking leaves into a big pile, and jumping in them in the fall. And he had heard what fun it is to watch the leaves burn, how they make a lovely light and the fine, sharp autumn smell of smoke.

All this Trumpet knew.

And he knew something else.

He knew about Christmas in the winter—and about Santa Claus and his reindeer and his tiny sleigh all filled with toys.

"Oh ho," thought Trumpet, all alone in his big cage. "I know what I want for Christmas. I want somebody to keep me company."

He thought about that very hard.

In fact, he thought about it too hard. Toward Christmas, he began to forget to eat.

Sometimes he even forgot to listen to all the things the children said to each other. And he stood with his back to them, dreaming and rocking to and fro.

The children were troubled by Trumpet's strange new ways. They asked the zoo keeper what was the matter.

"Well," said the zoo keeper, "I think Trumpet is lonesome. I think he needs someone to keep him company."

"If that's all," the children cried, "we can help Trumpet!"

They saved all their pennies for weeks.

They put on a Christmas show "for the benefit of Trumpet" and got hundreds of pennies for tickets.

They sold Christmas cards—

Shoveled snow off peoples' walks and driveways—

And ran errands at a penny an errand.

By and by, those children had the biggest pile of pennies you ever saw!

They took them to the zoo in wagons and doll carriages and wheelbarrows. Then they whispered mysteriously with the zoo keeper.

"No," they said.

And "Maybe"—

And at last, "Yes, yes, yes! That's the VERY thing!"

feeling very tired by now, "maybe Santa Claus doesn't come to animals in the zoo. Maybe I won't get any present at all!"

That was a sad thought for Christmas Eve.

Trumpet squeezed his eyes shut to keep back the tears.

The zoo was quiet now. All the other animals were sleeping.

For a moment Trumpet thought he could hear the snow falling outside. For a moment he thought he heard the stars making a noise like Fourth of July sparklers.

And then he didn't even *think* he heard anything.

Trumpet was sound asleep.

"At last!" whispered the zoo keeper. "Now for his Christmas surprise!"

On Christmas Eve, the zoo keeper tried to get Trumpet to sleep as soon as it was dark. Trumpet lay down in his straw bed, good as gold. But he did not feel one bit like sleeping.

He was much too excited about Christmas. He stared into the dark, wondering what Santa Claus would bring him.

"Maybe a boy to live with me," he thought. "Or maybe a girl."

But no, boys and girls have mothers who want to tuck them into their own beds at night.

"Maybe he'll bring me a pony," thought Trumpet.

But no, not even Santa Claus could find a pony big enough for an elephant to ride!

"Maybe," thought Trumpet, who was

Tramp-tramp-tramp! went some very big feet.

"Shush, shush, shush!" said the zoo keeper.

He led a very large, dark shadow through the dark, sleeping zoo. He opened the door of Trumpet's cage without making one single jingle of keys. And the big shadow tiptoed in, lay down right behind Trumpet, sighed a happy sigh, and went to sleep, too.

When it was morning, Trumpet woke up very early.

He rubbed his eyes and looked all around in the front of his cage.

"Oh," he cried. "Santa Claus *doesn't* come to animals in the zoo! He didn't come to me. He didn't bring me anything at all!"

And just as he said that, Trumpet felt something big and warm behind him. The big and warm something woke up and moved and smiled.

"Hello, Trumpet," it said.

Trumpet turned around.

There, right in his very own cage was a beautiful big gray elephant, with a big red bow on her neck and a sprig of holly in the bow, and a card with squiggles written on it.

"I wonder what the squiggles say?" whispered Trumpet shyly.

"I know," said the new elephant, "because the children read them out loud."

She told Trumpet that the card said:

THIS is CLARINDA, YOUR NEW WIFE, WITH A MERRY CHRISTMAS to TRUMPET beCAUSE WE LOVE HiM .... FROM ALL THE CHILDREN

Trumpet just smiled and smiled and smiled when he heard that.

And then his heart turned a big somersault, because Clarinda said, "I love you, too, Trumpet."

That was a wonderfully happy thought for Christmas!

"Why," said Trumpet, "why, it's even BETTER than having Santa Claus come!"

Clarinda nodded her head and smiled.

"Much better," she agreed. "If Santa Claus had brought me, he'd have had no room in his pack for one single toy!"

"That's right!" cried Trumpet, laughing at the very thought of his beautiful big new wife riding in Santa's tiny sleigh.

He made Clarinda laugh, too. They laughed until everyone in the whole zoo was awake and calling "Merry Christmas" back and forth.

And one Christmas—

Not *that* Christmas—

Not the next Christmas—

But the *next* Christmas after, Trumpet and his wife had a little baby elephant.

They asked the zoo keeper to put a ribbon on its neck, and a card that said,

MERRY CHRISTMAS
To ALL THE CHILDREN
BECAUSE **WE** LOVE THEM
....TRUMPET AND
CLARINDA

The keeper did.

And when the children saw that cute, funny, gay little elephant baby, they were almost happier than Trumpet and Clarinda themselves.

Almost, but not quite, because those two big elephants were filled with happiness from their big ears to their big toes.

And NOBODY could ever be happier than two elephants-full!

59

THE CHRISTMAS PUPPY

ONCE there was a puppy who lived in an alley between two brick walls. He ate whatever he found to eat, and he slept in a small empty box.

"It's quite a good bed," said the little puppy.

But one morning he woke up shivering. It was cold in the empty box. The north wind blew through the cracks and cried, "Get up, little puppy! It's winter now and you'll have to find a warmer home."

"That's just what I'll do," barked the little puppy, as he tumbled out of the empty box. "This is the day before Christmas. I'll find a nice warm home for my Christmas present."

He ran out of the alley looking for a warm new home.

When he saw some boys throwing snowballs, he ran right up to them. "Who wants a puppy for Christmas?" he barked.

But the boys only laughed and threw more snowballs. One snowball knocked the little puppy over and over in the snow. He scrambled to his feet.

And when the puppy tried to follow him, he said, "No, little puppy, you can't go home with me. I have no home either."

"Silly puppy," the wind whispered as it came back with a whooosh!

Now the little puppy ran up to the mailman, who was tramping along with his mail bag full of letters and packages.

"I thought boys liked puppies," he thought sadly.

Just then the wind came whistling around the corner. It blew up under the puppy's fur and shook his little ears until they looked like unraveling socks.

"Boys do like puppies," laughed the wind, "but they throw snowballs, too."

The wind twirled the puppy around so he could see a man sitting on a bench. When the puppy ran to him, the man got up and shuffled off through the snow.

"Oh, no, puppy," cried the mailman. "I can't take care of you. I have too many things to take care of already."

The wind blew the puppy out into the slippery street.

"Some people are too busy with packages to bother with little puppies," it whistled, and it tossed the puppy up against a policeman's big foot.

"Here, you," the policeman said. "Get back on the sidewalk before you get hurt."

61

He put the puppy on a big pile of snow on the sidewalk. There the little puppy felt colder than ever.

It was getting dark, and the lights were coming on in all the stores. People hurried by with their arms full of packages. They laughed in the merriest way, but no one noticed the little puppy.

"Everybody seems too busy to even look at me," he sighed.

And then a little girl ran up to him.

"Oh, Mother," she cried, "look at this darling puppy. Can't I take him home?"

The little puppy's heart leaped for joy.

And then it fell down into his cold little toes, because her mother said:

"A puppy would tear up your doll-house and scratch the rugs and break all the ornaments on the Christmas tree. Come along!"

The little girl ran back to her mother, and they hurried away in the falling snow.

The wind blew sleet in the puppy's ear.

"Some people have too many things to bother with puppies," sighed the wind as it tumbled him over and over again.

The puppy ran on among hundreds of people and double-hundreds of feet, tramping through the snow. Children scampered from store to store looking at toys in the windows.

"I hope I get that engine," cried a little boy. And a little girl sighed, "I think I will get that beautiful doll!"

"Bow-wow!" barked the little puppy. "Doesn't anybody at all want me for Christmas?"

But only the wind answered him.

"Shush! Some people are too busy wishing to bother with puppies!"

And it pushed him down a side street. The little puppy tried to run into the firehouse, but the wind pushed him back.

"Not there," said the wind. "They have a dog and five little puppies now!"

It blew him past the police station and across the railroad tracks . . . just ahead of a big engine that screamed "Loooooook out! Here I come!"

And then the wind blew the little puppy right out into the country.

It was dark now. The houses were far apart and the snow was deep.

"Oh, dear," he thought, "if I don't find somebody who wants a puppy pretty soon, Christmas will be gone."

"Hurry then," cried the wind, and it blew his woolly ears right out in front of his face.

He ran over a bridge and down a hill. He ran past houses with Christmas trees shining in the windows, with wreaths on the doors and smoking chimneys. Then he saw a dark little house with no Christ-mas tree in its window, no wreath hung on its door.

"Here, puppy," growled the wind. "If you're bound to be a Christmas present, you should have some Christmas wrap-pings, too."

It blew a bright piece of red ribbon toward him, and laughed and laughed as it whirled away.

The puppy grabbed the Christmas rib-bon and began jumping toward the door of the dark house. The trailing ribbon made two straight tracks from the side-walk right up to the door.

The puppy barked and barked on the doorstep. But no one opened the door.

"I guess nobody is home," he sighed.

He was too tired to go any farther. So he turned round and round to make a little hollow place for lying down, and then—

A big blanket of snow slid off the roof on top of the little puppy! It covered every bit of him and only the ends of the Christmas ribbon showed where he was.

"I'll freeze to an icicle," thought the little puppy. "I'll never live until I'm somebody's Christmas present! I'll never have a home at all!"

Then he heard voices near the road.

"Oh, Mother," cried a little boy's voice. "Santa Claus came while we were out. See the marks of his sleigh!"

His mother looked down at the ribbon tracks.

"I don't think those are sleigh tracks," she said in a tired way. "I just don't think Santa Claus would come away out here."

But the little boy was sure something magic had happened. He went running up the path.

And then he saw the Christmas ribbon sticking up in the snow. He scooped the puppy out of that snowdrift, red ribbon, cold paws, and all, and held him up for his mother to see.

Then the little boy snuggled that cold little puppy against his woolly jacket.

The tired mother smiled a real smile and ran up the path. Her eyes looked as bright as Christmas tree lights. She put her arms around the little boy and the little puppy.

"You did get your present after all," she whispered to her little boy. "Your little Christmas puppy!"

The puppy waggled his icy tail and wiggled his snowy ears and barked.

And the wind laughed merrily.

"Some people are glad to have cold little puppies for Christmas," it said, and away it blew.

THE ONE RED BIRD

NE red bird would not go south.

"Not I," said he. "The south is bright with flowers and fruit and the songs of birds. But the north is cold and still. Only the black, bare trees stand in the snow against gray sky.

"I will stay here.

"I will flash my bright feathers against the gray sky. I will sing in the quiet winter in the bare black trees.

"I will stay.

"I will stay."

But the wind blew cold—oh, cold.

The snow fell deep and white. It covered the grasses with their dry pods of seeds. The branches were ice-clad, cold and slippery to small bird feet.

Cold—oh, cold.

"What shall I do?" cried the one red bird.

The stars sang coldly.

Under the eaves clung the one red bird. And a little warm draft blew his ruffled feathers. Down he darted to a snowy window sill. The window was open—just enough for a small red bird to squeeze himself through.

Down he flapped to a warm house floor.

And across the room, shining with lights, stood a Christmas tree.

"For me! For me!" sang the one red bird.

He sat on the branches of spicy fir in the shining light.

Popcorn to eat!

And salted nuts!

A gingerbread man up near the top!

"Oh, I'll sing and I'll sing and I'll never stop," sang the one red bird on Christmas Eve in the glittering, glistening, shining light of the Christmas tree.

"For me! For me!" sang the one red bird.

"I will stay."

THE CHRISTMAS TREE LAMB

NCE upon a time there was a small, white, Christmas tree lamb.

He belonged to a grandmother when she was a little girl. He belonged to a mother, too, when she was small.

And when he belonged to the grandmother, he was a brand-new lamb. His fleece was snowy white against the dark branches of the tree. His black bead eyes shone with lights and excitement. And his shining hooves looked as if he might frolic from branch to branch the very next minute.

Besides all that, the tiny golden bell on his collar jingled merrily whenever anyone brushed against the tree.

That was splendid, that first Christmas!

The lamb was new. And the grandmother was little. And everyone said, "The lamb is the prettiest thing on the whole tree!"

There were lots of splendid Christmases.

But after a while, the lamb began to look dusty. After a while the grandmother was grown up. Then the Christmas lamb belonged to the mother.

She loved that lamb when she was little.

66

She played with him every year before she put him on the tree.

And one year, pop! one bead eye came loose and rolled into a corner.

The next year, crack! the Christmas lamb lost a leg.

Three years later, his tiny golden bell fell off, and was lost with the lost things of Christmas.

By the time the mother was grown up and had a little girl of her own, that lamb was in a sorry state!

He was gray with dust, and he had but one eye, two legs, no collar, and of course, no bell. But he was still a Christmas lamb, eagerly waiting to go on the tree.

The grandmother picked him up and said, "We can't put him on the tree any more!"

The mother took him and said, "No, he's nothing to look at now. But how pretty he was, long ago!"

Now the little girl reached out her hands for the lamb.

"How did he look?" she asked.

The grandmother told about his snowy white fleece.

The mother told about the golden bell that had jingled so merrily.

And the little girl could see for herself that a lamb should have *two* black eyes and *four* shining hooves.

So she took the lamb into her own room. She brushed and cleaned him until he was as white as the snow falling outside. She made him two new legs, and glued them on, and painted them shining black. She sewed a small black bead in place for an eye.

And she tied a bit of red ribbon around the snowy lamb's neck, with a new little golden bell in front.

When Christmas Eve came, the little girl crept downstairs with the lamb held behind her back.

She waited until the grandmother wasn't looking.

She waited until the mother wasn't looking.

Then she stood on a chair, and put the lamb on the Christmas tree, up near the top, right under the shining star.

67

When the grandmother saw the lamb, her eyes glistened. "He looks just as he did when I was a little girl," she said in a whisper.

The mother looked then, and her eyes sparkled.

"He looks much finer than he did when I was little!" she said.

The little girl didn't say a word.

She was too busy loving the lamb and thinking he was the prettiest thing on the tree. She touched the tree, and the lamb swayed to and fro. His two eyes shone with lights and excitement. His four hooves looked ready to caper from branch to branch.

And his new golden bell jingled more merrily than the old one ever had. Perhaps that was because the small, white Christmas tree lamb was happier than he had ever been in all his white cotton years on all the Christmas trees!

Sample Nepotism Policy

y of the company that no employee shall be employed in a position in which the employee must
y or indirectly to a family member (immediate or extended family), spouse, partner, significant
eone with whom the employee lives.
ployees should become spouses, partners, significant others, or choose to live together, one must
reports directly or indirectly to the other. Failure to voluntarily resign will result in the involuntary
of one of the parties at the discretion of management.

ame _____

ignature _____

_____

Therefore, everyone who works for, or represents, the organization (including board members, staff, committee members, and so forth) must sign a Conflict of Interest form.

This serves to raise the level of awareness that the organization does not tolerate or defend conflicts of interest. Additionally, this will encourage reporting of all real or perceived conflicts of interest. For the protection of everyone involved, these conflicts should be brought to the attention of the level of authority necessary for consideration, resolution, and direction.

Conflict of Interest Form

I have been informed of this organization's policy regarding conflicts of interest. I agree to bring to the attention of the proper level of authority any real, or perceived, conflicts of interest that may arise during the course of my tenure with this organization.

Such conflicts include, but are not limited to, personal or professional affiliations, relationships with family and friends, dealings with other organizations or businesses, political considerations, or relationships with other boards of directors.

Additionally, I agree to abide by the direction and decision of management. I understand that failure to advise management of such conflicts may result in disciplinary action, termination of employment, or removal from my position.

Name _____

Position_____

Signature _____

Date _____

Nepotism

Employing relatives is usually a very bad i
solution to a hiring issue, but it may very we
day-to-day tensions that can happen in th
likely to occur among family members than a

To protect your company, you probably s
the board. If that is not feasible, or desirable, y
a modified, department-specific policy. This
the employment of family members in any a
and, in particular, the accounting function.

The policy should also state that family mei
ferred into, positions where they will have di
another.

This will save you a lot of headaches and
future.

As with all forms and policies suggested in t
Policy and Nepotism form with a competent atto

It is the polic
report direct
other, or som
If two em
resign if one
termination

Employee N

Employee S

Date

Whistleblowers

There is evidence that the only reason some fraudulent acts were exposed was whistleblowers—someone came forward and reported known or suspected illegal activity.

With this in mind, an aspect of the Sarbanes-Oxley Act of 2002, prohibiting retaliation against whistleblowers, should be addressed.

As of the copyright date of this handbook, the Sarbanes-Oxley Act requires only public companies to comply with this policy. However, other businesses, non-profit organizations, and the like should give serious consideration to implementing a mechanism for reporting known or suspected fraud and a whistleblower protection policy prohibiting retaliation. A mechanism for reporting suspicious activity should be well thought out and written.

The policy itself should be included in the Employee Handbook, and employees should also be required to sign a form further strengthening the spirit of the policy.

Employee Handbook Policy

"All employees have a duty to report on suspected fraud or unethical activity to the appropriate level of management. Such reporting will be strictly anonymous and confidential.

Additionally, any retaliation against any employee who has reported on a suspicious activity will not be tolerated and the offending employee will be subject to disciplinary action and possible termination."

Review the Whistleblower Policy and form with a competent attorney.

Employee Responsibility to Report Fraudulent or Unethical Activity Form

An unfortunate aspect of our society is that fraudulent and unethical activity is a reality all organizations are subject to, and our organization is no exception.

The organization has a policy whereby all employees are required to report known or suspected fraud or unethical activity in a confidential manner, and retaliation against such employees is strictly forbidden and grounds for possible termination of employment.

Anonymous Reporting

All employees who become aware of actual or suspected fraud or unethical conduct have an obligation to report such activity to the appropriate level of management. This information will be held strictly confidential and the reporting employee will remain anonymous.

Retaliation Prohibited

If management becomes aware of any retaliation in any form against an employee reporting actual or suspected fraudulent or unethical activity, the offending employee will be subject to disciplinary action including possible termination of employment.

By signing this document, I acknowledge that I am aware that I have an obligation to report real or suspected fraudulent or unethical activity to the appropriate level of management, and that such reporting will be held strictly confidential and anonymous. I also acknowledge that retaliation in any form taken against such an employee will not be tolerated, and such action will be grounds for disciplinary action including possible termination.

Employee Name _____

Employee Signature _____

Date _____

Witness Name_____

Witness Signature_____

Date _____

Noncompete Agreements

Every company has competition. But you don't want to have a competitor on your staff. Therefore, it's important to have every individual associated with your company sign a Noncompete agreement.

Noncompete agreements should specify that employees should not be employed by, or have any type of relationship with, *a competing organization.* This prohibition will cover the period of time that the employee remains with you. Upon termination, the former employee must surrender all materials, documents, or information that would be of value to the competing organization. This information typically includes, but is not limited to:

➤ Financial information
➤ Sales materials
➤ Customer information
➤ Member information
➤ Mailing lists
➤ Equipment
➤ Confidential information
➤ Legal documents
➤ Personnel records
➤ Business plans
➤ Marketing plans
➤ Competitive data
➤ Original documents of any kind

Noncompete Agreement Form

I acknowledge that, during the course of my employment, I am prohibited from concurrent employment, or any other relationship with, any real or perceived competitor of the company.

   I also agree that, upon termination of my employment, I will surrender to the company all information, documents, or materials that would be of benefit to any competing organization.

   I also agree that I will not discuss any confidential information, knowledge, or data that I obtained during the course of my employment.

Name _____

Title/Department _____

Signature _____

Date _____

Supervisor_____

Signature _____

Date _____

Review this form with a competent attorney before implementation.

Confidentiality of Information

In almost any position in a company, an employee will be entrusted with confidential information. Consequently, it's in the best interests of all involved to have everyone sign a Confidentiality agreement.

Confidential information includes, but is not limited to:

- Financial statements
- Salaries and wages
- Contracts with vendors
- Lease information
- Credit information
- Banking relationships
- Insurance information
- Customer or member data
- Legal matters
- Personnel concerns
- Bid information
- Tax information and returns
- Personnel records
- Budget information
- Business plans
- New product development
- Competitive assessments
- Marketing plans and strategies
- Affiliations

The basic agreement should be simple and brief. Make sure that you review the agreement with your attorney to ensure that what you are implementing covers all aspects of confidentiality important to your company. At the same time, it is important that you do not inadvertently intrude on anyone's personal rights, so review the Confidentiality of Information form
with a competent attorney.

Confidentiality Agreement Form

It is the policy of this company to ensure that its operations, activities, and affairs are kept strictly confidential.

In the event that, during your employment, you acquire confidential or proprietary information and/or you are involved in confidential matters, it is understood that you will hold such information in strict confidence. Such information is to be discussed on a need-to-know basis only and exclusively with the staff person in authority.

Confidential information includes, but is not limited to:

- Financial statements
- Salaries and wages
- Contracts with vendors
- Lease information
- Credit information
- Banking relationships
- Insurance information
- Customer or member data
- Legal matters
- Personnel concerns

- Bid information
- Tax information and returns
- Personnel records
- Budget information
- Business plans
- New product development
- Competitive assessments
- Marketing plans and strategies
- Affiliations

By signing this agreement, I agree to the Confidentiality Policy and acknowledge violations of confidentiality will be subject to disciplinary action and possible termination.

Name _____

Title_____

Signature _____ Date _____

Supervisor_____

Signature _____ Date _____

Bonding Issues

It is extremely important for all organizations to have a Fidelity Bond, also known as Employee Dishonesty Insurance. The purpose of bonding your employees is to protect the organization, as a whole, in the event of internal embezzlement.

When you look into getting bonded, you need to make certain that the bond is adequate. You also need to know who is, and who is not, covered on the bond, and you should have a predetermined plan of action to follow in the event of a claim.

Who Should Be Covered?

It goes without saying the CEO, CFO, and other key employees with a lot of responsibility and control, should be included. In addition, I firmly believe that every employee who has *anything* to do with money coming into, or money going out of, the organization should be included on the Fidelity Bond. That even includes mailroom employees, front desk personnel, accounts receivable/payable clerks, and all check signers.

Officers and directors are often excluded from coverage. Know your bond and who is covered. Don't assume coverage for an important position. The coverage might not exist, particularly on your Chief Financial Officer, and you may be out on a limb without a net. (Refer to "Wire Transfers," in Section 4, for an example of what can happen if you are not careful with the details of your Fidelity Bond.)

How Much Is Enough?

The amount of the coverage, and the deductible per claim, will differ with each company. The two major factors to consider are the nature of the business and the level of its potential exposure. You should do a study to determine what a potential loss might total and ascertain the amount of the deductible you are prepared to pay per claim. Obviously, the amount of coverage and the deductible will dictate the cost of your coverage. Don't let cost, however, interfere with your good judgment. Protect your company and yourself.

When You Make a Claim

You must read the Fidelity Bond Policy. Too many of my clients rely on a staff person to check the policy details, while they look at the big picture. While this may be appropriate sometimes, it isn't when it comes to liability coverage. You need to thoroughly discuss all the provisions with your insurance agent. Legitimate claims are sometimes disallowed if the organization, among other things, fails to advise the insurance company in the proper manner, or fails to secure a timely police report.

Once the organization has flow-charted the cash trail and decided on the amount of coverage, you should meet with the insurance agent to discuss all the details, including excluded positions and claims procedures. Then you should determine how you are going to handle claims and the steps to be taken in the event of a claim. This will go a long way toward avoiding surprises in the event of a problem.

Other Issues

Finally, ensure that there are no relationships with other organizations that *require* the bond be at a certain monetary value. It is common for granting agencies to require the bond be set at the amount of the grant, banks often require set bond amounts, and so forth.

Tip: Explain to employees what a Fidelity Bond is and emphasize that when the organization subrogates its rights to the insurance company, the insurance carrier *will* prosecute.

Signers on Bank Accounts

In case you haven't noticed, most of the perpetrators of fraud work in the accounting department. Most of the examples throughout the book demonstrate this.

Therefore, it should come as no surprise that I recommend strongly that accounting personnel should never be check signers or wire transfer agents. Individuals who have access to checks, process checks, verify bank reconciliations, compute payroll, or handle any other financial function should never be authorized signers. It is much too tempting.

The best procedure for processing checks:

Step 1. The invoice is approved for payment.
Step 2. A check request form is completed.
Step 3. The CEO approves the check request.
Step 4. The check request is forwarded to accounting.
Step 5. Accounting processes the check.
Step 6. The CEO signs the check.
Step 7. A second designated employee (who does not approve the payment and is not in the accounting department) should cosign the check.

With this system, the company has four people involved in processing a check: the approver, the accountant, the CEO, and the second check signer. That makes a fraudulent transaction significantly more difficult to perpetrate.

Two-Signature Checks

Two signatures should be required on every check. This is vital for administrative and internal control purposes.

Requiring the second signature on every check simply means an extra pair of eyes is looking at each transaction. That limits the probability of either an honest error (such as an incorrect amount or unintentional double payment) or an embezzlement. It seriously limits frauds and embezzlement because collusion would have to be present, and that is rare. It is extremely risky for one individual to approach another individual to enter into a theft scheme.

Consequently, if there is embezzlement even when two signatures are required, it's very likely that the second signature is a forgery. Believe it or not, this is good for the organization. Forgery is a felony and is easily proved. Therefore, you have an easier legal case than if you are trying to prove theft.

Is One Signature Ever Good Enough?

How about requiring just one signature for checks written for small amounts, such as under $500? Not a good idea. It sounds as though it would help lighten the administrative load, but it can backfire. And I can attest to that.

During a consulting arrangement with a client to evaluate their internal controls, I suggested that they require two signatures on every check. Ignoring my advice, they decided to set up a policy that only required two signatures for checks over $1,000. Any amount under that would only require one signature.

Sounds reasonable. Right? Wrong.

A few weeks later, I sent them an invoice for $2,700 for my consulting fee. My payment came in the form of three checks, in the amount of $900 each and signed by only one person. The staff had found a way to expedite their check-processing procedure.

This is a great example of how the spirit of the policy varies from reality. The flow chart for processing a check should be as follows:

Check-Processing Procedure

➤ Invoice is approved for payment.

➤ Check request form is prepared.

➤ The CEO approves/signs the numbered check request form.

➤ Check request form is forwarded to accounting.

➤ Accounting processes the check.

➤ The check is signed by two authorized individuals.

➤ The check is mailed.

➤ The bank statements are sent to the CEO's home (or P.O. box) for review.

➤ The CEO forwards the reviewed bank statements to accounting for reconciliation.

In this scenario, two people are required for every check issued, which greatly reduces the probability of fraud.

Unless the organization is extremely large (and then you should have a computerized system), never utilize a check-signing machine or a signature stamp. Besides the obvious lack of internal control that results from these devices, fraudulent checks often involve forging a check signer's signature. This is a felony act that is easier to prove than the unauthorized use of a check-signing machine or signature stamp.

Lockbox

Most banks have a Lockbox Service, and businesses that receive checks and credit card transactions through the mail should give serious consideration to utilizing this service, so that organization employees don't come into contact with original checks.

Lockbox is an arrangement whereby remittances to an organization are actually sent directly to the organization's bank, rather than to the organization's physical address. Typically, the organization mails invoices to customers and provides an addressed remittance envelope. This envelope usually has the organization's name but, unknown to the remitter, the address is actually the bank's address.

The bank receives the remittances, makes a copy of the check, and deposits the original check. The copy of the check, envelope, and data in the envelope are forwarded to the organization with a validated bank deposit slip.

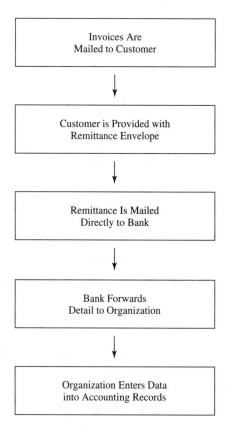

Once again, with regard to internal controls, Lockbox is very effective, because employees do not come into contact with original checks, virtually eliminating theft of these remittances.

There is an additional benefit to using Lockbox: Generally, most businesses receive remittances on a business day, but these receipts are not physically deposited until the next business day. If Lockbox is used, the bank deposits the receipts on the day they were received, and if the Lockbox account at the bank is an interest-bearing account, the organization will benefit from an additional day's interest. If an entire year's receipts benefit from this additional interest, this revenue will significantly offset the bank's fee for the Lockbox Service. When this interest earned factors in weekends and holidays, the financial benefit of using Lockbox really makes sense.

Positive Pay

Positive Pay is a relatively new service offered by most commercial banks, and it is probably the best internal control over check disbursements an organization can employ.

There are variations of this service, but basically:

1. The bank provides the organization with Positive Pay software.

2. The organization loads the software on its computer.

3. As checks are processed, important information is exported to the bank via a modem, compact disk, or other means.

4. As checks are presented to the bank, the information forwarded to the bank by the organization is matched against the checks. If the information presented does not match exactly, the bank will not honor the check without the organization's approval.

The essential information Positive Pay checks for includes:

➤ Payee is correct.

➤ The amount of the check is correct.

➤ Checks have not been duplicated and cashed more than once.

➤ Voided (Stop Payment) checks have not been presented for payment.

➤ There are no out-of-sequence checks.

➤ Expired checks have not been presented for payment.

Positive Pay, coupled with other effective internal control policies, such as requiring two check signers, prohibiting checks from being made payable to acronyms, prohibiting employees in the finance department from being signers, requiring check requests, having an independent review of bank statements, and so forth, will go a long way toward preventing check fraud.

Deposit Security and Restrictive Endorsements

As they arrive, checks should be put immediately under lock and key. They should never be left out in the open, on countertops or desks, where other employees or customers might have access to them. It has become very simple for a knowledgeable person to divert such checks for their own use.

Check This Out

Consider this scenario. The mail carrier leaves the day's mail on the countertop in the reception area. A new customer walks in and sees the pile of mail. Seizing the opportunity, the customer simply picks up the mail and walks out.

In the pile, there are several checks made payable to the ABC Service Company. Any embezzler knows that he or she can open a new bank account anywhere in the United States, in the name of the ABC Service Company. The embezzler can use the stolen checks as the initial deposit. Monitoring the availability of funds online, this person could write a check drawn on the newly opened account and end up with a lot of cash.

Checks Require Immediate Action

It never ceases to amaze me how often companies sit on checks before processing them. These checks are payments; delaying deposits can mean a loss of interest income, a chance that you are holding a bad check, or an opportunity for someone to execute a check fraud. So my first piece of advice is: **When a check arrives, act fast.**

Make sure *everyone* on staff (not just accounting personnel) knows that checks are the lifeblood of the business and, therefore, they take priority over everything else. Without those payments in your bank account, you just might not have anything else. So checks come first. (And, in my opinion, billing is a close second.)

Make certain that the mail is handled properly. Instruct the mail carrier (usually it's the same person, coming at the same time every day) that mail should not be left on a desktop. Have a buzzer to alert the backup person to the receptionist that the mail has arrived, or have a special, secure container where the mail can be placed.

Your Check Endorsement

Once the checks have been sorted from the regular mail, they should be immediately endorsed with a For Deposit Only stamp, a restrictive endorsement preventing them from being cashed. This prevents checks from being diverted, cashed, or used as a deposit. Altering an endorsed check is very difficult. (By the way, you should do this on all your personal and payroll checks as well. Just hand-write the information on the back, including For Deposit Only, and your check is safe until you get to the bank.)

Your endorsement stamp should spell out your organization's full legal name, under the words For Deposit Only. Never use an acronym. To keep your banking information confidential, you should *not* include the name of your company's bank or your account number on the endorsement stamp. That way, no one can find out this information from a cleared check. For example, assume your organization has been targeted by a clever scam artist. This individual purchases something from your organization with a personal check that was approved with a Telecheck machine. This person probably doesn't want or need what he or she has purchased, what they really want is their canceled check back when they get their next personal bank statement in the mail. If your endorsement stamp has your bank account number on it, *they* now have your bank account number, because it is on the back of their personal check. Armed with your account number, it is simple for the thief to print checks for a fraudulent entity with your account number! It can take a long time before this scam is discovered, and once it is discovered, the defrauded business has to close out the account and deal with the bank to recover the funds.

Sample endorsement stamp

FOR DEPOSIT ONLY
YOUR COMPANY NAME
(e.g., American Crayon Association, Inc.)

Once the checks have been endorsed and the deposit prepared, put everything under lock and key.

Check Deposit Security Procedure

➤ Checks are endorsed immediately with proper endorsement stamp.

➤ Deposit slip is prepared.

➤ Deposits are taken to the bank (or put in the safe until they can be deposited).

Often companies have multiple accounts. Consequently, the checks that are received are made payable to different payees. This makes endorsements more challenging. I advise initially depositing these properly stamped checks in your main bank and then transferring the funds to the other banks later. At a minimum, at least initially stamp these checks with a For Deposit Only stamp without the individual account name.

In all cases, endorsed checks should be forwarded directly to the finance department, not to the department responsible for the sale. If other departments need these checks, issue copies of the checks. Never release your originals to anyone but accounting.

A Note on Lockbox

I must remind you how valuable the Lockbox Service can be. If an organization uses a bank's Lockbox Service, employees never come into contact with original checks, thereby eliminating the possibility of diverting, altering, or cashing checks. See "Lockbox," in this section of this manual.

Check Stock

If you use the type of check stock that can't be scanned or that smears easily (if someone attempts to erase the figures), then you are ahead of the game. In fact, you are so far ahead, you can move on to the next chapter. If you don't use this type of stock, you need to know about scams that can occur. So read on.

Read This and Weep

In the following check-scanning scam, a check was made payable to the ABC Publishing Company in the amount of $20,000.

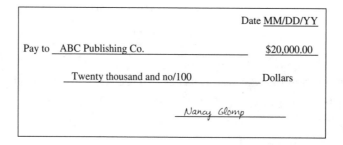

Someone, somewhere along the line, intercepted the check before it got to the publishing company. He effectively scanned the original check onto the same type of check paper stock. The scan was so perfect that it was hard to tell the difference between the original check and the eleven scanned copies.

The person who retrieved and scanned the check was part of a group of conspirators who were set up in several different states. These conspirators, each in possession of a scanned check, easily opened up bank accounts in their respective states, under the name of ABC Publishing. They used the scanned $20,000 checks as their "initial" deposit to activate the accounts.

They monitored their accounts electronically and waited for the deposit to clear the bank, making the funds available. Once this occurred, they quickly used the temporary checks supplied by the bank to access the funds. $220,000 was stolen in less than ten days, before anyone was aware of what had happened.

A Check Is Only As Good As the Stock It's Printed On

It is very important to invest in the type of check stock that can't be scanned. This kind of stock is encoded with the words "VOID" or "NOT AN ORIGINAL DOCUMENT," which are not noticeable to the naked eye. They will, however, appear on the face of the copy of the scanned check.

It's also surprisingly easy to erase words and numbers on checks and then replace them with different amounts. To prevent this from happening, you should invest in the type of check stock that smears very easily if someone attempts to erase the amounts.

All of this may seem very simple, and it is. It doesn't take much to protect yourself from a very basic, but devastating, scam.

Tip: If possible, consider a policy whereby the payee's *address* is printed on every check under the payee's name. Why? If someone steals or intercepts checks and attempts to open an account under the same name in another state, this should be noticed and viewed as suspicious by an alert bank representative.

Cash Transactions

If your business has cash transactions of any kind, you must have a method to ensure that all the cash you receive goes into the till and stays there. By their very nature, cash transactions are hard to control. Their lack of audit trail makes securing transactions even more challenging. As a precaution, most companies have a policy that specifies that all purchases be accompanied by a receipt. But that doesn't afford much protection in the long run.

Imagine that someone comes into a local chamber of commerce to purchase a directory. In all likelihood, the front desk is occupied by a clerk with little, or no, direct supervision. The customer pays cash for the book and is given a receipt.

Is there any guarantee that the cash will stay in the till? Not really. The employee could easily void the transaction by processing a refund, and then pocket the money.

The best way to prevent this, and other similar situations, is to discuss your concerns with your CPA firm. They will have some ideas that you can institute that will pay off. One will be to have a firm, written policy that all cash transactions require receipts.

And, best of all, they might suggest sending out a "secret shopper" who visits the chamber, pays cash for a directory, and is given a receipt. Then you can check the day's receipts to ensure that the transaction wasn't voided. If it was voided, you know that the individual who voided the sale (the clerk or someone else in the office) is pocketing the money. If the transaction was not voided, you can be comfortable with the knowledge that your policy is being followed and that the employee who handled the transaction is honest.

After the good news, also follow up with a short employee meeting the following day. First, discuss routine matters. Then call the clerk who processed the transaction to the front of the room. Announce that the customer who purchased the directory on the previous day was sent in by your accounting firm to test your cash policies. Reward the employee's honesty with a small bonus in his or her next paycheck. This is a good way to reward the honest employee and also to announce, diplomatically, that there is a mechanism in place to monitor cash as well as other types of transactions.

This small bonus may be the best money the organization has ever expended, because the entire staff has been made aware there are checks in place!

Cash Register Issues

If a clerk wants to skim money from a cash register, the least obvious way is to ring up a NO SALE transaction, take money from a customer, put it in the cash register, and remove it later.

The most effective way to discourage this practice is to have someone other than the cash register clerk close out the register at unpredictable times. When you are balancing cash receipts with cash register data, an overage rather than a shortage is cause for concern, because it may mean that an employee has taken money from customers and recorded a NO SALE transaction, intending to remove the money later.

Warning signs:

1. If the register has the type of display that can be rotated and the display is not visible to the customer, it makes it easier for the clerk to ring a NO SALE transaction, place the money in the register, and remove it later.

2. Be suspicious if loose coins are on or near the cash register. A clerk recording NO SALE transactions and placing the cash in the register has to keep track of how much was placed in the register so that the proper amount can be removed later. One manner of keeping track is by using loose change; for example, pennies represent dollars to be removed, nickels represent five dollar bills to be removed, dimes represent ten dollar bills to be removed, and so on.

Insurance Committees

As in the case of internal audits, an Insurance Committee is not an option for a very small company. These businesses are best served by seeking advice from a reputable insurance agent.

The purpose of an Insurance Committee is to assess the company's exposure in virtually every area of operation and to determine if the coverage is adequate. This process is very important if the company is serious about risk reduction. Typically, insurance coverage would include, but not be limited to:

1. Fidelity Bond (Employee Dishonesty)
2. General Liability
3. Officers' and Directors' Liability
4. Automobile
5. Errors and Omissions
6. Umbrella
7. Health
8. Life
9. Key Man

Whether the company is large enough to benefit from an Insurance Committee or simply relies on the advice of a competent insurance agent, insurance coverage should be reviewed in depth every year to protect the assets of the company.

With regard to fraud, the most important aspect of an annual insurance review is to study the provisions of the Fidelity Bond and have a predetermined understanding of the procedures the insurer requires in the event of a claim, such as:

1. Does the policy require the insurer to be advised of a possible claim within a certain time period?
2. Does the police department have to be notified within a certain time period?
3. Is a police report required?

The purpose of having this predetermined procedure is to ensure that the company does not inadvertently violate the requirements of the policy, possibly delaying or even eliminating a claim.

Computer File Backups

All computer records, particularly accounting detail, should be backed up daily and stored offsite. Easy to do electronically, this is probably one of the most important protections you can have.

Where's the Fire?

I was retained to study a company's system of internal controls. Something just didn't seem right to management, and they didn't know what was going on. I was brought in to spend a few days to figure it all out. I had some hunches, but decided to reserve judgment until I had the proof I needed.

Late one night, I was awakened by a call from my client. Someone had started a fire in the computer room. The fire department saved the building, but the computer was destroyed. And there were no backup records. Piecing together the accounting records was impossible. Other valuable data, such as email lists and inventory records, were also destroyed and reconstruction would take months. Without the facts, no one will ever know the real story.

Take a lesson from me. While this is not technically an internal control issue, it is closely related. So I urge you to have your information technology manager back up all computer records daily and store them off-site.

Check and Wire Transfer Signatures

Requiring two signatures for every check and wire transfer is a must.

Why? With this policy in place, collusion is necessary to process a fraudulent transaction. Additionally, if a fraudulent check is processed and two signatures are required, there is a strong possibility that one of the signatures is a forgery, which is relatively easy to trace.

Also, the second signature means that another pair of eyes is looking at each transaction, so the possibility of detecting honest mistakes such as duplicate payments, incorrect amounts, or so forth, is enhanced.

Treat your transfers in the same manner that you would your checking account. The same procedures apply and will help you stave off problems in the long run.

Sample Policy On Check and Wire Transfer Signatures

In order to employ the strongest internal controls possible, the company has a policy that requires two signatures on every check processed or wire transfer requested.

The procedure for check requests and wire transfer requests is as follows:

➤ An authorized employee submits a Check Request or Wire Transfer Request.
➤ The request must be approved by the chief executive officer.
➤ The request is processed by accounting.
➤ Two other authorized signers will sign the check or wire transfer.

Employee Name _____

Signature _____

Date _____

Inventory Issues

Unfortunately, many companies do a physical inventory only at the end of the year. If there has been any inventory "shrinkage," it will be too late to investigate the matter and take corrective action. Inventory pilferage can really add up. With that in mind, periodic inventory valuations throughout the year are essential.

Although time-consuming, inventory checks are not difficult. The following are some suggestions that my clients have found helpful:

1. At least one of the inventory valuations should be a surprise and conducted at an unexpected time—for example, the middle of the month or after hours.

2. An occasional "secret shopper" can test certain internal control policies related to dealing with customers purchasing merchandise.

3. Just counting the items in inventory during a valuation is not sufficient. You should actually open a random selection of boxes containing inventoried items. It is possible that a customer could place an expensive item in an inexpensive package. Or an employee, after hours, could switch expensive items with less expensive ones and have an accomplice, acting as a customer, pay for the less expensive item when checking out.

4. If possible, have the items in inventory sealed in clear plastic. This not only prevents soiling, but it also makes switching items much more difficult. In lieu of this, seal boxes with inexpensive prefabricated aluminum foil or heavy-duty clear tape.

Company Credit Cards

Strict policies should be enforced with regard to employee credit cards. All employees must submit the credit card detail with any transaction record. Most companies only require the summary transaction record, which only lists the total amount. In those cases, management really has no idea what the employee purchased.

One of the most common occurrences is an employee getting around a policy that doesn't reimburse for alcoholic beverages. If the employee just submits the transaction summary, alcoholic beverages could have been purchased and no one would know. On the other hand, the credit card detail of the purchase is itemized.

Credit card statements should always be mailed to the CEO off-site. The CEO should review the credit card transactions and investigate unusual ones.

Credit cards can be more than an annoyance; they can be a real liability. They get lost. Card abuse is common. They can get stolen. And an employee who is leaving the organization can rack up substantial personal expenditures. These charges are easy to detect, but not easy to collect.

Consider getting out of the employee credit card business. Most companies are beginning to do just that. Employees can use their personal credit card for business expenses. Of course, your business should be prepared to reimburse employees quickly, especially for big-ticket items or expenses. In addition, if an employee purchases office equipment or furnishings, you should request all backup information. That would include, among other things, warranties and repair information.

Although there are some considerations and inconveniences when employees do not have a corporate card, eliminating them will significantly reduce the risk associated with credit card use and abuse.

Lines of Credit

Two authorized signatures should be required to activate a line of credit. One should be that of the company's CEO (or that person's designee). The other should be the company's CFO, who would normally be the one initiating the letter of credit advance.

This policy reduces the possibility of abuse and protects everyone involved, particularly the CEO and CFO.

You should also require a written authorization for the line of credit request. Use the form shown, and keep it in a separate binder for easy reference and referral.

Letter of Credit Activation Form

A request for a Letter of Credit advance in the amount of $_____

Requested from_____(Financial Institution)_____

The purpose for activation of this credit line is:_____

Requested by:

Name _____

Title_____

Date _____

Approved by:

Name _____

Title_____

Signature _____

Date _____

Second approval by:

Name _____

Title_____

Signature _____

Date _____

Bad Debt Policy

Customer A sells golf equipment and buys an ad in your organization's magazine for $1,000. An employee of your organization (let's call him B) has account receivable write-off authority; he is also a friend of Customer A. Every company experiences a certain degree of bad debt write-offs. Customers go bankrupt, reorganize, get seriously in debt, or die. A policy addressing write-off procedures is imperative. Why? Because it is very easy for a knowledgeable individual to arrange for "side deals."

On the side, Employee B and Customer A agree that, in exchange for a $500 golf bag, Employee B will arrange to write off the accounts receivable and cancel the advertising debt. Employee B could simply charge the accounts receivable against the Allowance for Bad Debt account. If he were even cleverer, he could charge an expense line item or reduce a revenue account by the debt amount. This would make his actions much more difficult to trace, particularly if the organization is not audited by a CPA firm.

To avoid this type of situation, a formal Bad Debt Policy should be established that includes the following provisions:

➤ Accounting personnel should never have the authority to cancel debt.

➤ A Write-Off of Bad Debt form should be completed, signed by the appropriate individuals, and retained for audit trail purposes.

➤ The CEO, or that person's designee, should personally approve all write-offs.

➤ Finance implements the write-off only after procedures have been followed and signatures acquired.

➤ Records should be maintained of all vendors whose debt has been canceled. Prohibit future dealings until the debt has been paid.

Write-Off of Bad Debt Form

Vendor _____

Address _____

Invoice No (s). _____ _____

Amount due $ _____

Reason for cancellation of indebtedness: _____

_____

Requested by _____

Approved by _____

Internal Audits

Very small companies would have difficulty justifying the necessity for an Internal Audit Committee, but nonprofit organizations with an active board of directors and a sizable employee base should give it serious consideration. The last thing you need is surprises at year-end. An Internal Audit Committee can provide non-profits with that necessary additional level of internal control throughout the year.

Even if an independent CPA firm audits your nonprofit organization, your board of directors ultimately has fiduciary accountability for the organization. By creating an Internal Audit Committee, you provide your board with another level of assurance that the organization's financial affairs are being managed effectively. This is especially true because an Internal Audit Committee is typically chaired by your treasurer, and that gives the board direct representation. The treasurer is privy to virtually everything that is going on financially within the organization.

Once established, the committee begins to work with the CPA to formulate an Internal Audit Plan that will specify, in detail, the committee's responsibilities. At a minimum, the committee should be responsible for the following:

➤ Have cut-off bank statements mailed directly to the treasurer in advance of the audit.

➤ Review the prior month's bank reconciliation in detail.

➤ Ensure that the organization's internal control policies are effective and, more importantly, being followed.

➤ Meet with representatives of your bank to review signature cards, to ensure that all signers are authorized and that there are no unauthorized accounts.

➤ Meet with your insurance agent to ascertain that coverage is adequate for all policies, with particular attention to the Fidelity Bond.

➤ Test the payroll by comparing payroll records to personnel files.

➤ Contact each employee directly to ensure that there are no "ghosts on the pay-roll."

➤ Interview all employees who are responsible for receiving and disbursing checks, to ensure that policies and controls are adequate and being followed.

➤ Test disbursements to ensure that invoices have ben approved for payment properly.

➤ Check the accounts payable files and physically contact new vendors to ensure that they exist.

As part of the ongoing procedure, the committee and the CPA should meet to discuss the management letter. The committee is responsible for preparing a report for the board that addresses all of the issues noted in the management letter. This report must also include the status of the resolution of each of the issues.

The internal audit should be scheduled between the last day of the CPA's field work and the date the CPA is expected to begin the next audit—"the window of opportunity"—because it is the period when most fraud occurs. It is also important to conduct an *unannounced* audit. That way, anything unusual in the finances will show up.

At the conclusion of the audit, the committee will prepare an in-depth report of their findings. The formal internal audit report should be reviewed with the chief executive officer and chief financial officer at the conclusion of the audit. In addition, the audit committee report should be shared with the board and the independent CPA firm.

In these times of concern about any organization's financial management, an Internal Audit Committee is relatively easy to put in place, but will create tremendous rewards in the long run. It is one good way to have financial peace of mind.

Stop Payment Orders

It may seem very academic, but you should always check current banking regulations for stopping payments on checks, debit memoranda, and wire transfers. Stopping payments can only be done for legitimate reasons. Doing so for improper reasons, such as simply delaying payments, may be a crime.

If, because of a stolen or lost check, a Stop Payment order is necessary, it is best to follow the method recommended by the American Institute of CPAs and the American Institute of Banking:

1. Make detailed notes covering the circumstances surrounding the reasons for the Stop Payment and what action was taken.

2. Complete a Stop Payment request form and process the Stop Payment order immediately.

3. Safeguard all documentation received from the bank. Maintaining this information (which includes dates and original signatures) could be very important in the event the bank fails to stop payment when advised.

Stop Payment Request Form

Date _____

Check # _____   Check date _____

Amount of transaction $ _____

Reason for stopping payment:_____

_____

_____

_____

Requested by _____

Title _____

Approved by_____

Title _____

Voiding Checks

When a check needs to be voided, you should always follow the five simple guidelines established and approved by the American Institute of CPAs and the American Institute of Banking:

1. Complete a Voided Check form.

2. Write the word VOID, in permanent ink, across the front of the check.

3. Cut off the signature line. This doesn't allow room for a microencoded check amount and ensures that the bank won't accept the check.

4. Mark the back of the check, in permanent ink, with the words: VOIDED CHECK, DO NOT DEPOSIT.

5. Start a Voided Check file that includes:

   ➤ The original voided check
   ➤ A completed and signed Voided Check form

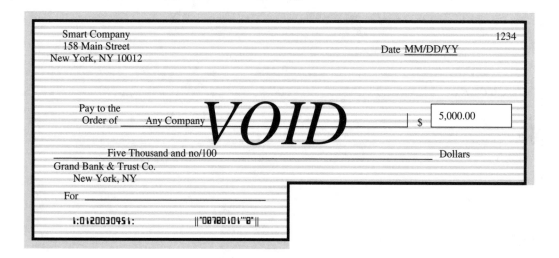

Voided Check Form

Date _____

Check # _____   Check date _____

Amount of check $ _____

Reason for voiding check: _____   _____

_____

_____

_____

_____

Requested by _____ ____

Title _____ ____

Date _____

Approved by_____

Title _____

Date _____

Numbered Check Request Forms

It is advisable for all CEOs of any company to personally sign a Check Request form for all disbursements.

The purpose of the form is to ensure that the CEO is aware of disbursements. But it also serves as a mechanism for the CEO to become familiar with vendors, or question unusual transactions before the actual check is prepared and mailed.

In addition to improving internal controls, Check Request forms provide a good audit trail for each transaction. For added security, invest in an accounts payable software program that requires a check request number before the physical check can be printed.

Check Request Form
No. 4733

Date _____

Requested by _____

Amount $ _____

Make check payable to _____

Purchase order number _____

Details of purchase: _____

_____

_____

Authorized by _____

Signature _____

Expense Accounts

A simple way to divert funds is to embellish, or "pad," travel reimbursement or expense accounts. It is often difficult to monitor these expenses because there is no real audit trail. Consequently, it is imperative that you institute a solid, written policy regarding what you consider appropriate, reimbursable travel expenses and expense accounts.

Expense Account Allowances

One viable option is to grant expense account allowances to select employees. A monthly allowance requires much less paperwork, and it's a predictable, controllable cost. The burden is on the employee to maintain proper records, and that frees up company personnel from handling those tasks.

But there are possible income tax ramifications to handling expense accounts in this manner. To properly adhere to the tax law, employees are required to track and account for expenses paid. If they fail to do so, the expense account allowance is considered taxable income to the employee.

The best way to avoid this is to have the employees complete a monthly form detailing their expenses and provide receipts for actual expenses paid. At the end of the calendar year, if the amount of excess expense account allowance exceeds $600, the employer is required to issue a Form 1099 to the employee for the excess, and the employee is required to claim it as income. Monthly reporting allows you, and the employee, to monitor the amount expended and make the necessary accommodations before year-end.

Travel Reimbursements

If you don't want to pay falsified or improper travel expenses, it's imperative to have strict policies and monitor these policies closely. Without an audit trail, it is realistically very difficult to control travel reimbursement requests. By instituting some of these ideas, you will be a long way toward doing so.

Per Diems   To eliminate tedious bookkeeping that comes from monitoring meal expenses, give employees a fixed amount per day (per diem) for meals. The easiest way to arrive at that amount is to find out the predetermined meal allowance stated by the federal government for each city. Then give that meal allowance to the employee in the form of a travel advance.

Assume that the per diem meal allowance for a city is $40 per day. If the employee will be in that city for three days, the travel advance for meals for the trip would be $120. If the employee spends more than $120, he or she will have to pay the difference. If the employee spends less, he or she can keep the difference. In either case, there is no additional record keeping involved. Receipts are not required under a per diem arrangement.

Food-Only Reimbursements   All employees are required to substantiate meal expenses with receipts, if they are on business. Your organization should have a "food-only, no alcohol" reimbursement policy. Require employees to submit a detailed restaurant receipt for reimbursement, including the credit card charge summary. That way, all expenses are revealed and unauthorized purchases can't be hidden.

Common Carrier Fares   One of the easiest ways to overstate air fares occurs when an employee uses a travel agency to arrange trips. All that is needed is for the employee to get an itinerary from the travel agency for a trip with an expensive carrier and submit that itinerary for reimbursement. Then, without your knowledge, the same employee goes to a different agency to purchase a ticket with a discounted carrier or uses a free frequent flier ticket.

It's not difficult to guess who pockets the difference at your expense. Unless you take on the task of arranging for the tickets and paying the fare directly, the only way to control this situation is to reimburse these expenses with the original airline receipt that is always issued with the ticket. An itinerary or a boarding pass would be unacceptable.

Predetermined Travel Budget   When you plan to reimburse consultants, speakers, or others, you can control costs by negotiating an all-inclusive fee that covers travel expenses. For example, assume that a company negotiates with a consultant to travel from City A to City B for a period of five days for an all-inclusive travel reimbursement of $2,000. In this case, the company simply records the entire fee as a line item travel expense and sends the consultant a 1099 for the $2,000. This method requires far less paperwork because the traveler has the responsibility to keep the receipts and tally the account for the travel expenses on his or her own tax return.

Expenses without Receipts   Whenever possible, always require original receipts for all expenses. For those expenses that typically do not have receipts (such as tips, mileage, and so forth), you need to make policy decisions about the level of the expense you will accept. In these cases, you will be relying on the honesty of your employee. Fortunately, these expenses are usually easy to spot, and the risk of loss to you is small.

CPA Management Letters

Your auditing CPA firm is not hired to uncover fraud. If they should do so coincidently, that's all well and good. But, ferreting out fraud and embezzlement is not their function.

First and foremost, they are hired to issue an opinion on the financial statements. However, during the course of audit field work (particularly while they are studying the system of internal control), it is very likely that your CPA will notice areas of concern. If these areas are significant and reach the level of a reportable condition, the CPA is required to advise the board of directors in the form of a Management Letter.[1]

Auditors are not clairvoyant. It is perfectly acceptable, and even recommended, that the CEO discuss internal control issues of concern with the auditor. As the head of your organization, you should be privy to the contents of the Management Letter before it is reviewed with your board of directors. You never want to be blindsided by a negative Management Letter at a board meeting.

By way of example, let's assume that the auditor discovers poor internal controls regarding bank statement processing. At present, bank statements are sent directly to the CFO, who is also a check signer. Only one signature is required on a check, which makes this a very dangerous combination.

Is the CPA required to report this situation in the Management Letter? Yes. Does it reflect poorly on the CEO? Definitely! Is there anything you can do? Absolutely! Correct the problem!

Since the poor internal controls existed during the year under audit, the CPA is still required to advise your board of directors. However, instead of using language that implies poor management, the wording would now appear as follows: "During the course of the study of internal controls, a weakness was detected in the areas of bank statement security and check signers. However, we are pleased to report that management has taken action to correct the deficiency."

The CPA has advised the board of a reportable condition, but, at the same time, the CEO is in control and is very proactive in the eyes of the board.

Your CPA should discuss the Management Letter issues directly with the board when the financial statements are presented. For the protection of everyone involved, particularly you and your CFO, this discussion should be very straightforward. Remember, the CPA works for the board of directors. Your auditors work through you and your CFO, but they work for the board. Be aware of the issues they raise to the board, so you will be able to correct them quickly.

An effective Management Letter addresses the issues bluntly and, where possible, offers suggestions for improvement. Document any changes you would like to implement, and ask your CPA to include those as part of the Management Letter. All CPAs will work with you to improve controls. Today, it has become a matter of course. Due to increased responsibilities placed on them to prevent fraud, CPAs will even go as far as to threaten an organization with a Qualified Audit Opinion, if there are inadequate internal controls.

---

[1] Management Letters are not restricted to internal control issues, and routinely reflect unrelated areas of concern such as tax issues and the like. Due to the nature of this book, only the internal control aspect of the Management Letter is addressed.

Random Disbursement Checks

In the course of auditing your company, your independent CPA should verify disbursement transactions as follows:

1. Record the number of checks written during the year under audit (the check population).

2. Visually examine each check, looking for unusual amounts, strange vendors, or suspicious checking endorsements.

3. Statistically determine the number of checks (sample of the population) that must undergo thorough auditing procedures. If the sample passes all audit checks, the auditor can assume that the population of checks would also meet auditing standards.

4. Via a computer program, enter the beginning and ending check numbers, to provide random numbers that encompass the sample.

5. Apply required audit procedures to the random sample:

   ➤ Obtain original signatures of all check signers for the audit file.
   ➤ Determine that check request procedures and approvals have been followed.
   ➤ Ensure that the sample check numbers appear on the bank statements.
   ➤ Make sure the amounts of the checks match the amounts on the bank statements.
   ➤ Match the signature on the check with the original signature in the audit file.
   ➤ Match the check number, payee, and amount against the check register.
   ➤ Audit supporting documentation (such as invoices and statements) to check for required approvals.
   ➤ Determine that new vendors physically exist by making phone calls or checking addresses.
   ➤ Examine the endorsement stamp to ensure that the check was endorsed by the intended payee.
   ➤ Compare endorsement stamps for the same payees with other checks.
   ➤ Examine the bank clearinghouse stamps.
   ➤ Check that the bank's microencoded check amount matches the check amount.
   ➤ Perform additional auditing procedures for checks where the bank has made an encoding error.

To close up the window of opportunity for fraud, the CEO should conduct a modified version of these audit procedures on a monthly basis:

1. Have accounting provide the beginning and ending check numbers for all checks written during the month.

2. Check that the beginning check numbers follow the ending check numbers for the prior month, and investigate any unaccounted-for checks.

3. Follow auditing procedures the CPA applied to the sample.

4. Request all supporting documentation, particularly invoices and statements, for the check selected.

5. Always thoroughly investigate new vendors to ensure that they exist.

6. Check all unusual or large transactions.

Because most thefts occur between the time the auditor completes the work at the end of one auditing year and the beginning of the next year's audit, the practicality of doing routine examinations of disbursements during this period is inarguable.

CHECK 21

In 2004, the United States Congress passed a law titled CHECK 21.

Background

The passage of CHECK 21 was a direct result of the September 11, 2001, tragedy. Prior to the passage of the law, original checks cashed by payees were sent from the payee's bank to the originator's bank and eventually included in the payee's bank statement. For example, if a business located in California remitted a check to someone in New York, the New York bank had to physically transport the original check back to California after having presented the check for payment.

After September 11, however, airplanes were grounded for an extensive period of time, effectively paralyzing the entire financial network of the United States.

To ensure that this would not occur again, CHECK 21 was passed.

CHECK 21

CHECK 21 is a system whereby cashed checks are not physically transferred from the receiving bank to the originating bank; instead, an *image* of the check is transferred electronically. Important: This check image is considered the legal equivalent of the original check and as such can be entered into evidence during court proceedings and so forth.

Check Images

Depending on the originating bank, account holders will now receive one of the following:

1. A simple bank statement with no checks or check images enclosed. Usually these banks have check images available online.

2. A bank statement that includes images of only the fronts of checks.

3. A bank statement that includes images of the fronts and backs of checks.

Internal Control Issues

Generally, businesses should always arrange to get images of both the fronts and backs of checks included with their bank statements, even if they are charged a bank service fee. Why? Endorsement comparison is an essential audit tool, and to be precluded from examining backs of checks would prevent auditors from:

1. Determining if employees are signing checks over to third parties.

2. Determining where employees are cashing checks.

3. Ensuring that a vendor's endorsement stamp is consistent and that no one has opened an account in another bank under the same name.

Note: Items 1 and 2 may be indications of "ghosts" on the payroll or employees with financial difficulties.

Clever Examples
of Embezzlement

Payroll Tax Deposits

YOU MUST CHECK your payroll tax deposits on a periodic basis to make sure they are accurate. Why? Simple. If you don't know how payroll tax deposits work and don't have deposits audited periodically, you are asking for trouble.

A Taxing Example

A local nonprofit seemed to have effective internal controls. Bank statements were mailed to the CEO's home. The CEO reviewed all the checks that cleared the bank and the bank statement. The bookkeeper was not authorized to sign checks. So far, so good.

With only four employees, it was easy for the bookkeeper to prepare the payroll checks weekly. She presented them every Friday morning for the CEO's signature. The payroll checks were always perfectly accurate, so the CEO signed them and personally passed them out to the staff.

Simultaneously, the bookkeeper prepared a check request for the federal payroll tax deposit, which included Social Security, Medicare, and Income Tax Withheld.

Check Request for Payroll Tax Deposit

Amount: $1,410.00

Payable to: U.S. Treasury

Description: Payroll Taxes for payroll period covering _____ to _____

Approved by _____

Title _____

Date _____

Later that day, the bookkeeper prepared the federal tax deposit check and gave it to the CEO for signing. The required tax deposit coupon was included with the check.

```
                                                                          1234
    Smart Company
    456 Main Street                              Date  MM/DD/YY
    New York, NY 10019


    Pay to the                                              1,410.00
    Order of ____ U.S. Treasury _____  $ _____


    _____ Fourteen Hundred Ten and no/100 _____  Dollars


    For _____        J. Roosevelt_____

    1:0120030951:      ||"08780101"8" ||     1239
```

When the CEO received the bank statement and canceled checks, he saw that the check had been deposited by the IRS and had cleared the bank. Assuming that all the effective controls were in place, the CEO had no reason to suspect that a major embezzlement was taking place right under his nose.

How? The tax deposit amounts were wrong. Since no one was checking the tax deposits for accuracy, there was a simple, but effective, embezzlement opportunity. The bookkeeper made an intentional overpayment in the amount of $300 on every tax deposit check. That meant that every week an overpayment of $300 was sent to the IRS.

At the end of every quarter, the bookkeeper prepared the Form 941 federal payroll tax return, as well as the state returns. The CEO signed the returns personally, but never had the returns checked for accuracy.

At the end of the year, the bookkeeper prepared the W-2 forms and, once again, the CEO never had the W-2s checked for accuracy.

The bookkeeper simply recorded the weekly overpayments as federal income tax withheld on the payroll tax returns. She noted the $15,600 total weekly overpayments as federal income tax withheld on *her own personal W-2 form*. When she filed her personal Form 1040 income tax return, she received a personal income tax refund check in the amount of—you guessed it—$15,600.

When the dust settled, it was discovered that the bookkeeper had been doing this for 25 years!

How It All Unraveled

Interested in knowing how the embezzlement was discovered?

This scheme ran for 25 years, resulting in a combined total of almost $400,000. It wasn't discovered until the bookkeeper got greedy.

The offending employee retired on August 17, and was owed $25.00 for expenses she paid on behalf of the organization. She prepared a check request for reimbursement, and her boss approved it. She later prepared a handwritten check payable to herself, and her boss signed it accordingly.

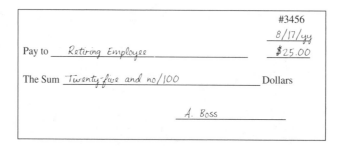

She took the check to the bank later that day, endorsed it, and prepared a deposit slip. Unknown to anyone, she wrote the check out with a pen with erasable ink and she erased the amounts.

She now had a check payable to her signed by her boss with no amount written. Incredibly, she altered the check to $35,000 and deposited it into her account!

The significance of the 17th of the month was that she knew the bank's cut-off date for mailing the bank account was always the 15th of every month. She had almost a full month to cover her tracks.

Altering a handwritten check is easy, but preventable if certain basic controls are in place such as:

1. Using a bank's Positive Pay service. The bank's computer would have detected that the amount was changed and would not have honored the check when presented.

2. Although old-fashioned, check imprinters still work. A check imprinter is an inexpensive piece of equipment available at any office supply store. Simply dial in the amount, insert the check and pull the lever. The check will be imprinted with THE SUM $25.00 in blue and red ink, and the check will also be perforated, preventing altering.

3. Handwritten checks should be written with a gel pen rather than an ink pen. A knowledgeable person could tape over the signature and dip the check into a common household liquid that would eradicate the ink, and then dry the check with a hair dryer. Once it is dried, a perpetrator could make the check out to whomever he wants and for any amount! Always use a gel pen instead of an ink pen for handwritten checks.

Discovering the $35,000 altered check was easy. It simply appeared in the bank statement a few weeks later. When the altered check was found, I was called in to check any other occurrences. One of the first areas I audited was payroll. The random tax deposit indicated a $300 tax overpayment, which prompted me to research more tax payments. It was odd that all of them had the $300 overpayment. I traced the overpayments to the federal income tax withheld on the quarterly Form 941 payroll tax return and, eventually, to the federal income tax withheld on the bookkeeper's personal W-2. Voilà!

If the bookkeeper had not altered the $35,000 check, the payroll tax scam would probably never have been detected.

More importantly, this situation could have been avoided if the CEO had arranged for a periodic check of the payroll tax deposits and tax returns. Additionally, this serves as a good example of what can happen if a company doesn't have an annual audit by a CPA firm. The board of directors felt that they didn't have the budget, and that there was no need for an audit. So, to save the $5,000 annual audit fee, they lost $15,600 every year for 25 years. That's why I always tell my clients that it is better to be safe than sorry.

A Clever Variation

A business owner meets with a customer who gives him a $2,500 check as a deposit on an item.

On the way to the office, the owner stops at the bank and deposits the check personally. He asks the bank to copy the check for him and gives the check copy and deposit slip to the staff accountant. The accountant takes the information from the owner and pockets the $2,500!

How is this possible?

Simple. If the accountant had handled the transaction properly, she would have increased cash and credited a revenue on a deposit account. However, she instead increased cash properly but credited the state withholding tax liability account, and sent the $2,500 in with the next state withholding tax deposit. She then included the $2,500 as additional state withholding taxes on her personal W-2 and received the money in the form of a state withholding tax refund.

Check Switching

Make sure that someone other than a finance employee reviews bank statements. As previously stated, at a minimum bank statements should be mailed to the CEO's home for review. For larger organizations, however, having copies of bank statements, with the corresponding canceled checks, sent to a secured Post Office box accessible only to the CEO or members of the internal audit team for review is unquestionably *the* most important internal control for businesses of any size. This allows the CEO or auditors the opportunity to examine each individual check and review any suspicious transactions.

Sound overzealous? It's not. With computerization, it's simple to replace checks that are issued for legitimate purposes with phony ones. An unsuspecting CEO (and even an experienced auditing CPA) would never know the difference. The importance of the CEO reviewing bank statements and checks became apparent during the course of my very first fraud examination.

Experience Is the Best Teacher

As a course instructor, I was asked to spend some time reviewing basic internal controls for a class of CEOs. I had no actual fraud examination experience at the time, so I dusted off an old auditing textbook for some suggestions. One piece of advice stood out from all the others.

The next day, I told my class that all CEOs should have their company's bank statements mailed off-site. They should then take the responsibility for reviewing the statement and all the cleared checks, before sending them on to accounting for bank reconciliation purposes. Little did I know that this advice would initiate my career as a fraud examiner. Note: After reviewing Section 6 of this manual, "Identity Theft," I feel that it is actually much safer to have the copies of the bank statements mailed to a Post Office box rather than someone's home, unless the individual's personal mail box is secured.

One CEO in the class took my suggestion seriously. She went to the bank after class to change the name and address on the statement, from the staff accountant's name at the office to her name at her home address. Wisely, she decided not to mention that she had changed the procedure to anyone, particularly the staff controller.

The following week, she received the first bank statement at her home. Not dreaming that embezzlement was taking place, she was shocked when she saw that check 1234, made payable to, and endorsed by, the staff controller, had cleared for $2,000. And, to make matters worse, someone had forged the CEO's signature on the check. Clearly something was wrong, and she wisely did not confront the controller at this point.

Since I was the one who had given her the advice about reviewing the statements, the CEO decided to call me to help her investigate the situation. Over the next few weeks, we jointly uncovered a brilliant embezzlement scheme that had earned the controller in excess of a half-million dollars and that launched my career as a fraud investigator.

What We Did

It was obvious that something was seriously wrong, but neither of us had any idea what. I decided to examine the accounting backup for the check 1234 by reviewing the check register. The check register records indicated that the check was payable in the correct amount of $2,000, but the office records showed the payee as the U.S. Postal Service! Looking further into the situation, I found that the actual accounting records verified that there was an approved check request for the postage check in the files, and an actual postal receipt was stapled to the check request.

We then went to the bank. We decided that the best course of action was to copy the front and back of the canceled check payable to the controller and put the original check back in the bank statement. At our request, the bank changed the address on the statement back to the controller's name at the company's address and remailed it immediately. Clever, huh?

Two weeks later, I went back to the company. I went to the file cabinet where the bank statements were stored and found the statement that the bank had resent two weeks earlier. Opening the statement, I discovered that check 1234 had been removed and replaced with another check (also 1234) for the same amount. The substitute check was payable to the U.S. Postal Service, and even had a post office cancellation stamp on the back, showing that it had been cashed by the post office.

It was clear that the scam involved the post office. To further investigate, I reviewed all bank statements for the prior three months. I made copies of every check that cleared the bank through the post office (all of which appeared perfectly legitimate). We then got copies of the bank's copies of these checks. Several of the bank's copies were payable to the controller, while the office copies were payable to the U.S. Postal Service!

How It Was Done

When the controller was confronted, she confessed to the embezzlement and told us how she did it. Brilliantly, she was able to fool both management and a very competent, experienced independent CPA firm that audited the company's records.

She ordered a supply of checks from a check printer. Then she went back to the check printer several weeks later and told them that a temporary agency had cleaned the office and, by mistake, had thrown out the printed checks. She reordered a new supply of checks that were identical to the first set; same color, same account number and, most importantly, same check numbers.

As you probably suspect, she kept the first set of checks in the office and the second set of checks at her home. The organization wrote a lot of checks for postage, including checks for the postage meter, the bulk mail account, media mail, the business reply account, and so forth. The office policy stated that the CEO had to sign each check request and each corresponding check. The controller was not authorized to sign checks.

One day, the controller presented the CEO with a routine check request for $2,000 for postage, which the CEO approved.

CHECK REQUEST
Date:MM/DD/YY
Amount: $2,000.00
Payable to: U.S. Postmaster
CEO Approval: G. Lincoln

After getting approval, the controller wrote the check and presented it to the CEO for her signature.

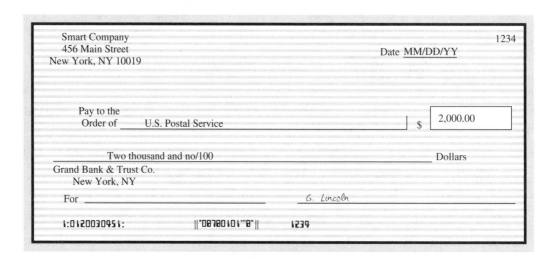

The controller now had the approved check request and the signed check in her possession. She put the signed check in her purse. She took the diskette out of the office computer and took it home with her. That evening she inserted the diskette into her home computer, where she had installed the same check-processing software. Using the duplicate set of checks, she scrolled up, on her display, to check 1234:

Check # 1234
Amount $2,000.00
Payee U.S. Postal Service

She placed the cursor at the end of the payee's name and erased the U.S. Postal Service as the payee, leaving the payee line blank:

Check # 1234
Amount $2,000.00
Payee

Then, she simply typed in her own name as the payee:

Check # 1234
Amount $2,000.00
Payee Jane E. Doe

She hit the Print key and printed the check:

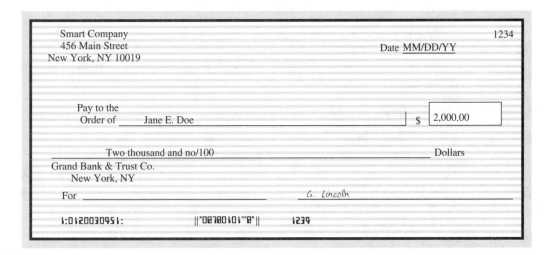

Smart Company
456 Main Street
New York, NY 10019

Date MM/DD/YY

1234

Pay to the
Order of _____ Jane E. Doe _____ $ 2,000.00

Two thousand and no/100 _____ Dollars

Grand Bank & Trust Co.
New York, NY

For _____   G. Lincoln _____

1:0120030951: ||"08780101'"8|| 1234

Then she did the simplest thing in the world. She forged the CEO's signature. Please remember that it is physically impossible for banks to match checks presented for payment against original signature cards. Banks process millions of checks every day, so comparing checks against signature cards is a physical impossibility. It is the businesses's responsibility to ensure that checks are signed properly, not the bank's.

She endorsed the check and cashed it at a bank other than the company's bank, which made it more difficult to detect the forged signature. This simple scheme, performed repeatedly over the years, resulted in a gain to her of over $500,000.

Why the CPA Didn't Discover It

The controller was an experienced accountant who knew what the CEO did, and did not, review. She also knew the CPA firm's auditing procedures, and she had the control of the bank statements—a dangerous combination.

She knew that CPAs are hired to catch inconsistencies and discrepancies in financial reporting. They are hired to verify that the financial statements are accurate. They are *not* hired to check for falsification or to catch fraud. She was well aware that a CPA's checklist of audit procedures, with regard to auditing disbursements, would involve these activities:

1. Review check request approval procedures, check signing authority, and other procedures, to ensure that they are followed.

2. Witness individuals signing checks with their signatures for the audit file.

3. Follow Generally Accepted Auditing Standards to ensure that a large enough sample of checks is audited statistically.

4. Make sure that the audit samples (randomly selected checks) correspond to those on the bank statements by number and amount.

5. Look for proper check endorsements.

6. Verify that the check is backed up with a valid receipt.

7. Check to see that bank clearinghouse stamps appear on the backs of the audit sample.

8. Make sure that the bank's microencoded amount on the bottom front of the check (after the preprinted account number, ABA routing number, and check number) matches the written check amount.

The falsified check 1234 ended up in the audit sample. After a thorough review, the auditors concluded that the check was genuine because:

1. A check request was signed by the CEO.

2. The approval signature matched the CEO's original signature in the audit file.

3. Check 1234, for the correct amount, appeared on the bank statement detail.

4. The CEO's signature on the check itself appeared authentic.

5. The check was endorsed by the post office.

6. There was an authentic postal receipt in the file.

7. The back of the check also was affixed with the bank clearinghouse stamps.

8. The check had the correct microencoded amount of $2,000.

```
Smart Company                                          1234
456 Main Street
New York, NY 10019
                                          Date   MM/DD/YY


Pay to the
  Order of   U.S. Postal Service                      $2,000.00


Two thousand and no/100                               Dollars
Grand Bank & Trust Co.
     New York, Ny


For _____          G. Lincoln

1:0130030451:      11'03750101"8'11     1234         200 000
```

How Was All This Possible?

The mysteries were unraveled as I completed the investigation.

How did she encode the checks? The answer lies in how the bank corrected erroneous coding of checks. They taped a piece of white tape, with the correct amount over the incorrect amount. All the controller had to do was find an old check with the correction tape, remove the tape from the old check and tape it on the bottom of the fraudulent check. Of course, she had to find an old corrected check with the proper amount first, so it took some sorting time for her to make her scheme work.

And how did she get clearinghouse stamps on the checks? Simple. The controller went to a rubber stamp supplier and had them made. They looked exactly like authentic clearinghouse stamps, and they fooled everyone, including the auditors.

How did she make all this work through the U.S. Post Office? One word—collusion. A postal employee simply endorsed the back of the fraudulent check with the actual postal endorsement stamp! No auditor in the world could catch this because the endorsement stamp *was* the postal endorsement stamp.

With regard to a receipt, the postal employee simply recorded a $2,000 transaction, producing a receipt given to the thief, and then voided the transaction, resulting in no traceable sale at the post office.

And, finally, how did she get away with it for so long without getting caught? It's really quite simple. The controller knew the system, and that system was within her control. She was an experienced, well-qualified, and apparently loyal employee.

The CEO had a great deal of faith in her abilities and gave the controller even more responsibilities. This led to the CEO giving up a great deal of control. Under many circumstances, this would be fine. But if there is a lurking embezzler in your finance office, it could spell trouble. And finally, why didn't this excess postage look suspicious on the internal financial statements? Simple. When the controller concocted the scheme years ago, she started at a mere $100, but over time she gradually raised the amount to $2,000. In the interim, since the controller was in effect the budget coordinator, she literally was able to budget in the annual embezzlement, so the internal financial statement appeared to be in line.

The End Result

With the overwhelming evidence, the CEO confronted the controller and pressed charges. The controller, as well as the post office accomplice, received prison terms.
    Case closed.

Ghosts on the Payroll and Ghost Vendors

Ghost Employees

If the right controls are not in place, it is relatively easy to place a nonexistent or unauthorized person on a payroll and pocket the money. As long as the perpetrator is not greedy, this scam can go undetected for long periods of time.

Ghosts are typically put on the payroll by someone who actually prepares the payroll, or by the manager of satellite offices who has the authority to hire people and can simply forward fraudulent employment documentation to the parent office for processing.

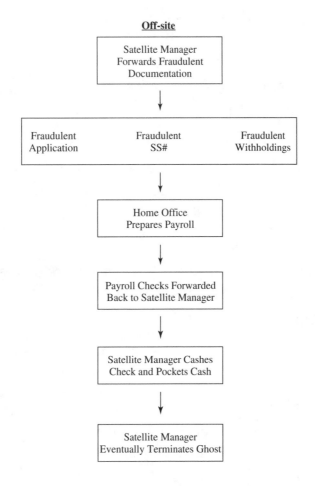

Off-site

Satellite Manager
Forwards Fraudulent
Documentation

Fraudulent
Application

Fraudulent
SS#

Fraudulent
Withholdings

Home Office
Prepares Payroll

Payroll Checks Forwarded
Back to Satellite Manager

Satellite Manager Cashes
Check and Pockets Cash

Satellite Manager
Eventually Terminates Ghost

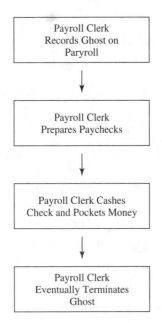

Payroll Department

Payroll Clerk
Records Ghost on
Paryroll

Payroll Clerk
Prepares Paychecks

Payroll Clerk Cashes
Check and Pockets Money

Payroll Clerk
Eventually Terminates
Ghost

Steps to take to prevent ghosts on the payroll:

1. **Employment Application**

   Ensure that the organization's employment application is thorough and that the "employee" fills it out completely and no spaces are left blank.

2. **Social Security Number Check**

   Always request the applicant's Social Security card and follow that up with an independent check of the number. There are databases that enable employers to check on Social Security numbers.

3. **Reference Check**

   Ensure that someone checks the personal and professional references noted on the employment application.

4. **Credit Check**

   Make sure that the employment application states that the employer has reserved the right to run a credit check of the applicant.

5. **Time Sheets**

   Time sheets are not popular, but they are practical. Ensure that time sheets are signed by both the employee *and* the supervisor.

6. **Direct Deposit of Payroll**

   Seriously consider requiring employees to participate in Payroll Direct Deposit. As noted in the warning signs that follow, often ghost employees do not deposit payroll checks into bank accounts, lessening the probability of detection. One aspect of Direct Deposit of Payroll is that the employee is *required* to have the net check deposited into a bank account, making a ghost employee scheme somewhat more difficult.

7. **Distribution of Payroll Checks or Deposit Receipts**

   If possible, payroll checks or deposit receipts should be distributed to employees by someone other than the person who prepared the payroll or the off-site satellite manager.

8. **Independent Check of Employees**

   At least once a year, have the payroll checks or deposit receipts distributed by the organization's CPA or a member of the Internal Audit Committee, to prove the existence of all employees. This should be done at a time between the auditors' conclusion of audit field work for one year and their return to start field work for the next year. See "The Embezzler's 'Window of Opportunity'" in Section 1 of this manual.

Obviously, a clever person in the right position can circumvent the checks noted. However, there are a few patterns and warning signs of potential ghosts on the payroll.

Warning Signs

1. Remember that the individual who has placed a ghost on the payroll has done so for the purpose of stealing the net paycheck. Therefore, the perpetrator will arrange to have the net paycheck as high as possible, by:

   ➣ Having little or no federal or state income taxes withheld by claiming a high number of dependents on Form W-4.

   ➣ Having no voluntary deductions for insurance, savings bonds, charitable contributions, and so forth.

2. The ghost on the payroll is almost always a part-time employee, because full-time employment complicates things by triggering such things as health insurance applications, life insurance applications, disability insurance applications, and so forth.

3. The ghost on the payroll is almost always employed and terminated during the course of one calendar year, lessening the chance discovery by auditors. They are "rehired" after the auditors have completed their field work. (See "The Embezzler's 'Window of Opportunity'," in Section 1 of this handbook.)

4. Checks made payable to ghosts on the payroll are usually not deposited into a bank account, lessening the probability of detection. Look at the back of payroll checks—checks that are cashed at check-cashing services or liquor stores, or signed over to a third party, or the like are *always* suspicious.

5. The surnames of ghosts on the payroll are frequently very common names such as Smith, Jones, or Miller, lessening the chances of name recognition detection.

6. Employment applications for ghosts rarely note a spouse.

7. Employment applications for ghosts often don't list an actual address, but rather list a post office box address or a nonexistent address.

8. Employment applications for ghosts rarely note a land-line telephone number, but rather note cellular telephone numbers that are easily terminated and hard to trace.

9. Employment applications for ghosts often don't note prior employers but rather note "stay at home dad" or other excuses to account for employment absences.

A Little Humor   Fraud is a serious problem, of course, but occasionally there are instances of humor.

This really happened.

A car dealership employed over 100 people. The business was not audited, and the payroll clerk was virtually unsupervised, a dangerous combination.

It seems the payroll clerk had her husband, who was in a building trade, fraudulently on the payroll as a part-time employee for *fourteen years!* (It would be easy to hide a part-time employee for a business of this size.)

How was the husband ghost detected?

It seems the husband accepted a job in another state, and his wife went with him. The husband, not knowing how the system works, *filed for state unemployment!* Of course the state sent an employment verification to the business, and this is how the ghost was discovered.

Ghost Vendors

A deterrent to being victimized by a ghost vendor scheme is to have a thorough, current, and updated Approved Vendor File. At a minimum, vendor information on file should include:

> Full legal name of vendor
> Street address
> Contact name
> Business telephone number
> Fax number
> Email address
> Website address
> Federal Identification Number (FIN)

As in the case of ghosts on the payroll, perpetrating a ghost vendor scheme usually requires the perpetrator to be in an upper-level position or in the finance department. A ghost vendor scheme is relatively simple:

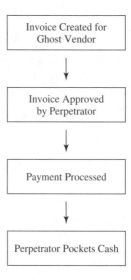

A deterrent to a ghost vendor scheme is to have the independent auditors validate the existence of new vendors the organization has been doing business with since the conclusion of the previous fiscal year.

Verifying the existence of new vendors is relatively easy:

1. Physically visit the new vendor's offices.

2. Contact Dun & Bradstreet for business data.

3. Research corporate records.

4. Research public databases.

5. Check with the bank where the checks have been deposited.

6. If the vendor's invoice notes a PO box address, inquire at the post office as to the owner of the box.

Warning Signs

1. As in the case of ghosts on the payroll, perpetrators of ghost vendor schemes almost always arrange for fraudulent payments between the times the auditors conclude audit field work for the prior year and start audit field work for the subsequent year. (See "The Embezzler's 'Window of Opportunity'," in Section 1 of this handbook.)

2. Usually, phony invoices for ghost vendors have a post office box remittance address rather than a street address.

3. Attempts to call the ghost vendor usually reach an answering machine.

4. Often, invoices from ghost vendors do not include information typically included on legitimate vendor invoices such as:

   ➤ FAX numbers
   ➤ Email addresses
   ➤ Website addresses

5. Sometimes originators of phony invoices use consecutive or very close invoice numbers.

Tip: A simple but hard to detect ghost vendor scam is to first prepare a check payable to an approved vendor and later prepare a check for the same invoice with a clever variation of the approved vendor's name. For example:

Approved vendor name: ABC Service *Corp.*
Variation: ABC Service *Co.*

The best way to avoid this type of ghost vendor scheme is to randomly compare endorsement stamps on the back of checks looking for variations, different account numbers, and the like.

The Danger of Acronyms

Any entity that you do business with should be instructed to make its checks payable to the full legal name of your company. Even if your company is widely known by its acronym, actively discourage your customers, or members, from making checks payable to it.

The best way to learn that lesson is by example. Here it is.

For years now, the American Crayon Association has referred to itself as ACA. Therefore, its customers and members routinely make checks payable to the acronym. The accounting clerk receives the checks, gives the customers or members credit in the accounting records, prepares the deposit, and takes the deposit to the bank.

Pretty straightforward and foolproof. Right? Wrong. This can result in a serious problem.

Let's just assume for a moment that the accounting clerk needs cash for a personal matter. So he comes up with a scheme. He goes to a bank in a nearby city, presents the proper paperwork, and opens up an account under the name Acme Creative Advertising, another ACA. The clerk then deposits some of the checks payable to ACA into his new account.

He can hide the stolen payments any number of ways. He can take the ordered product from inventory and mail it out personally. Or he can pretend that the checks are a bad debt and write the money off existing accounts receivable. As long as the clerk doesn't get too greedy or careless, no one will know the difference.

This activity is very difficult to detect. Beware and be wise—follow these suggestions:

1. Use your bank's Lockbox Service. Employees don't come into contact with checks mailed to the company, so diversion of these checks is virtually impossible.

2. Request that customers and members make their checks payable to your company's full legal name.

3. Your endorsement stamp should appear as follows:

```
FOR DEPOSIT ONLY
YOUR COMPANY NAME
(e.g., American Crayon Association, Inc.)
```

4. The stamp should include the full legal name of your organization, but *not* your bank name and account number. Any dishonest person could draft a check payable to your company, and then pick up your bank name and account number when their check is cashed. The embezzler could then have fraudulent checks printed with that information microencoded on them.

5. Note that the endorsement stamp includes "Inc." I strongly recommend using "Inc." because someone can easily divert a check by depositing it into an account under the name American Crayon Association, LLP. So use your full legal name. It's safer.

6. Endorse the back of checks as soon as possible after receipt.

7. Make sure endorsed checks are only delivered to accounting. If the department responsible for the sale needs the check for verification, it can be given copies.

As is the case with having checks written to your acronym, processing checks payable to a vendor's acronym is also risky. If, for example, your company incurs a legitimate debt in the amount of $10,000 to the Allied Business Corporation (also known as ABC), your payment of that debt could be in jeopardy. All an embezzler has to do is intercept the check, deposit it into an account in another bank for, let's say, the Associated Building Council (another ABC). Then, when the funds become available, the embezzler just draws down the account.

You will lose out on two counts. You won't find out about the misappropriation until it's too late to track it down. Therefore, recovering your money will be virtually impossible. And your vendor still has an existing balance. Even though you have just fallen victim to a theft, you still have an obligation to satisfy the original debt.

So, to avoid this type of misappropriation, make sure all checks include the vendor's full name (with its legal distinction) and the street address. In addition, always check your mailroom security.

Bank Account Reconciliations

Not only should CEOs receive bank statements off-site and review them, they should also see all statement reconciliations.

The following scenario will show you how easy it is to perpetrate a fraud, if the bank reconciliations are not routinely reviewed. And it can happen even if your business is audited by an independent CPA firm.

It's December. The company operates on a calendar year. An invoice for a legitimate printing bill is approved for payment and sent to the CEO with a Check Request form. The CEO forwards the documentation to the finance department for check preparation. A check for $5,000 is prepared, signed by the CEO (plus a cosigner), and mailed to the EZ Printing Company, which cashes the check.

On the sly, the company accountant processes another check for the same invoice in a different check run. This check is put in the safe and not mailed.

In come the auditing CPAs. If they discover the second check, they will bring it to the attention of the accountant. Of course, he's prepared with an excuse. It's the last month of the fiscal year. Everyone is busy with the budget, preparing payroll tax returns, typing W-2s, and so forth. This was just a simple mistake. So he retrieves the check from the safe and voids it.

If the auditors don't catch the intentional duplicate payment, the second check will appear on the December bank reconciliation as an outstanding check. All the accountant has to do is be patient, wait for the CPAs to finish their audit file work, and issue the financial statements. Once this is over, the accountant can forge the check signers' signatures and cash the second check payable to the EZ Printing Company by opening up an account in another bank under that name.

The probability of the auditors discovering this is very slim. The original check was outstanding on the December bank reconciliation, which had already been audited by the CPAs. They wouldn't spend much time on a previously audited year-ending bank statement.

This type of scam is very difficult to stop. The perpetrator has a believable, built-in excuse if the double payment is caught. The only sure way to uncover it is for the CEO to check the bank reconciliations. Any unauthorized outstanding checks would stand out like a sore thumb. It's well worth your time and effort.

Wire Transfers

Meeting with your bank on a regular basis is just good business. It's the best way to ensure that your company is receiving the optimal bank service. It also gives you the opportunity to check the bank's records regarding your authorized wire transfer signers (as well as authorized check signers). You might be in for a surprise.

A Coast-to-Coast Horror Story

A not-for-profit organization applied for, and was awarded, a sizable grant from the state in excess of two million dollars (if you can't relate to a grant, insert Letter of Credit or something similar). The CEO signed the grant contract, and the funds were then available to be drawn down. When the grant was awarded, the staff accountant told the CEO that he had no grant accounting experience and was uncomfortable with that responsibility. The CEO thanked him for his honesty and advertised for a new CFO. Two weeks later they offered the job to a qualified applicant who accepted the position. The CFO was not a check signer nor an authorized wire transfer agent.

A few months later, after gaining the confidence of the CEO and staff, the CFO told the CEO that bank examiners were having the bank contact certain customers to update their bank records, and the organization was required to file new check signature cards and wire transfer agreements. The documents presented to the CEO noted the authorized signers' names and titles and, once again, the CFO was not an authorized signer.

```
┌─────────────────────────────────────────────────────────────────┐
│                      Wire Transfer Agreement                       │
│                                                                    │
│         Name                 Title                  Signature      │
│                                                                    │
│     P. Leahy            President          _____  │
│     J. Crowley          Treasurer          _____  │
│     H. Stuhldreyer      Vice President     _____  │
│     _____        _____       _____  │
│     _____        _____       _____  │
│                                                                    │
│                 Corporate Secretary _____         │
└─────────────────────────────────────────────────────────────────┘
```

Seemingly, this was just a routine bank request, so the CEO signed the document, along with the other approved signers—the corporate treasurer and the vice president. With the addition of the signature of the corporate secretary (as required by the bank) and the imprint of the corporate seal, the paperwork was complete. But not the scheme.

After getting the required signatures, the CFO then simply typed in *his name* and title and signed the document. The bank wasn't updating its records; the CFO told his bank contact that the organization was updating *its* records. Because he appeared to have authority, the bank gave him the documents. The CFO was now an authorized check signer and wire transfer agent, only no one knew it!

```
┌─────────────────────────────────────────────────────────────────┐
│                      Wire Transfer Agreement                       │
│                                                                    │
│         Name                 Title                  Signature      │
│                                                                    │
│     P. Leahy            President          P. Leahy                │
│     J. Crowley          Treasurer          J. Crowley              │
│     H. Stuhldreyer      Vice President     H. Stuhldreyer          │
│     C. Smith            CFO                 C. Smith               │
│     _____        _____       _____  │
│                                                                    │
│                 Corporate Secretary  J. Jackson                    │
└─────────────────────────────────────────────────────────────────┘
```

The CFO then proceeded to make legitimate wire transfers through one particular bank employee, and over the next few months they developed a natural business friendship.

Then, one Friday afternoon, at exactly 1:45 PM Mountain Time, just before the bank closed (any transactions after 2:00 PM would be recorded the following Monday), the CFO entered the very busy bank lobby. He gave his "favorite" bank employee a sizable wire transfer to a bank in California that, once processed, would virtually wipe out the organization. At exactly 1:45 PM Pacific Time, his partner in crime in California transferred the money out of the country—approximately 1.5 million dollars.

The scheme surfaced the following week, but it was too late. And, the situation went from bad to worse.

The organization filed a claim with the insurance company that handled its Fidelity Bond. They discovered that the bond excluded officers and directors. After retaining an attorney to prove that the CFO wasn't technically an officer, because he didn't have a vote on the board of directors, they were finally able to negotiate that hurdle.

Then, they discovered that the bond coverage was only for $500,000. Unfortunately, the embezzler stole over 1.5 million dollars.

And it didn't end there. When the state was advised of the missing grant funds, they decided to sue the CEO and the individual board members personally for reimbursement, because they had the legal basis to do so. The grant contract stipulated that the organization had to carry a Fidelity Bond for the full amount of the grant, and the organization hadn't bothered to check on it.

And finally, if the situation seems as though it couldn't get any worse, it did. There was no resolution in spite of the thorough investigation following the incident. No one can uncover the true identity of the perpetrator. Everyone knows it was the CFO, but his documents and personnel file were completely made up! This incident was a setup from the moment the individual applied for the position. In the end, they will never be able to find the perpetrator for prosecution.

A Word to the Wise

To protect yourself, the board, and the company, employ the services of a knowledgeable attorney to review every contract before it is signed. Periodically, visit the bank to check the bank's records and the current signature authorizations. If you receive bank documents that require signatures, cross out blank spaces with a marker so no additional names can be added. And, routinely review the adequacy of, and exclusions to, your Fidelity Bond. You have it for your protection, but, as is the case with any insurance policy, it needs to be reviewed and amended periodically to be of value to you and the organization. And finally, always perform a complete background check on any individual who will be employed in your accounting area. When all is said and done, you never know whom to trust with your company's money.

Postage Issues

The way the world is today, we have to look at every situation as a potential hazard. That even includes the relationship your company has with your local post office.

I know what you are thinking. If you can't trust the U.S. Postal Service, whom can you trust? Well, probably no one, when it comes to your finances.

A Bad Working Relationship

There was a CFO who perpetrated an elaborate check-switching scam that involved a second set of checks and an accomplice who worked at the post office (see "Check Switching," in this section). Even with other procedures in place (such as having the bank statement mailed to the CEO off-site, a proper endorsement stamp, and a visual check that there was no tape over the encoded area indicating a bank error), the perpetrator was still able to get away with the scam—with a little help from his friend.

In another example, an accounting clerk went to the post office and purchased a postal money order with a check from his company. This eliminated the need for an elaborate check-switching operation, or a postal worker accomplice. The check would clear the bank with a proper endorsement stamp and bank clearinghouse information. The microencoded amount would be authentic. Life couldn't get any easier for the embezzler.

The Trouble with the Mail Today

You also have to worry about what is happening in your own mailroom. While playing golf at a famous resort, one CEO arranged to have his picture taken with a client, as a gift.

To expedite delivery of the present, he wrote a note and hand-addressed an envelope, asking the mailroom clerk to run it through the postage meter. The CEO picked up the print later that day, put it in the prepared envelope, and dropped it off at the local post office. As he was putting it in the mail slot, he noticed that the clerk had metered the envelope for $37.00 instead of $37¢.

When he asked the post office clerk what could be done, he was told to turn in the postage meter tape on the envelope, and he would get a refund of $37.00 less a 10% handling fee. His pleasure at receiving the $36.30 refund changed to displeasure when he learned that his mailroom employee was getting refunds on a routine basis. Let's just call this "Post Office Petty Cash."

To prevent postal abuse, you will need to institute tight procedures that are reviewed by someone knowledgeable in postal abuses. At the very least, you should have an arrangement, in writing, with your postmaster that no one in the company is allowed to purchase postal money orders with company checks or obtain refunds for overpayments. When they do occur, the refunds should be credited to your account.

Kiting

Did you realize that if you arrange for periodic deposit audits, you will take the appropriate measure to prevent check kiting? In a very simplistic example, here's how a kiting scheme works:

Day One   An organization receives receipts totaling $20,000.

Receipts are entrusted to the finance department, which enters the deposit accurately in the accounting records.

A dishonest accountant, however, doesn't take the deposit to the bank on the following business day. Instead, he or she pockets the receipts.

Day Two   Receipts total $25,000.

Once again, the accountant pockets the $25,000.

Day Three   Receipts total $22,000.

The accountant uses $20,000 out of the third day's receipts to cover the $20,000 deposit for the first day. He or she keeps the extra $2,000 as a "slush fund" to balance subsequent deposits.

Day Four   Receipts total $25,000.

The accountant applies this total, plus $2,000 from the slush fund, to cover the second day's deposit of $25,000.

End of the Month   At the end of the month, the accountant pockets the total receipts from the last two business days of the month. This time, he or she records these receipts as "deposits in transit" on the bank reconciliation.

The accountant prepares the internal financial statements. The statements have been misstated by kiting deposits (covering them with subsequent deposits) and showing the last two days' receipts as outstanding items. At this point, the accountant has absconded with four days' worth of receipts.

This system of combining kiting of receipts and phantom deposits in transit is very difficult to detect. It is extremely difficult to reconstruct, particularly if it is done over a long period of time, and the organization is not audited.

An Ounce of Prevention

➤ Utilize a bank's Lockbox Service. Kiting receipts and falsifying deposits in transit on the bank reconciliation is virtually impossible with a Lockbox Service, because employees never come into contact with original receipts.

➤ Have an audit conducted by a competent CPA firm. In the course of an audit, the CPA will perform a "proof of cash" auditing technique that is designed to expose kiting and improper deposits in transit.

> ➤ Have the CPA firm come in, unannounced, during the middle of the year to do a thorough audit of an interim period. It is also important to arrange for a cut-off bank statement.

> ➤ Have the receipt clerk's responsibilities assumed by another employee on his Management Day off.

Manual Checks (Handwritten and Typed)

Handwritten or typed checks are vulnerable to alteration of the check amounts.

Computer-generated checks protect the amounts by imprinting a series of dollar signs to the left of the check amount so that additional numbers cannot be added. The words spelling out the amount of the check start on the far left of the line and end on the far right, so that words cannot be added. This protection is not afforded in any other check-writing method.

The Case of the Retiring Bookkeeper

A trusted bookkeeper was planning to retire in a year. Her husband had retired a year before, and started a retirement business called The Paper Clip Delivery Service. They lived in a rural Texas town. Every two weeks, he drove to Houston, where he was able to get favorable prices for his clients from a national office supply store that didn't deliver to this town. As payment for his services, he received a $25 service fee from his clients. One of his clients (as it turns out, his only one) was his wife's employer.

The bookkeeper told her boss that they needed to transfer $35,000 from an interest-bearing account to their disbursing account, which was a routine occurrence. The CEO signed the transfer slip. Unbeknownst to the CEO, the bookkeeper kept the signed transfer slip, but didn't make the transfer.

```
Funds Transfer
    Transfer: $35,000.00
    From: Account #234567
    To: Account #345678


                                    Signature: J. Johnson
                                    Date: 3/17/yy
```

Months went by, and the bookkeeper's retirement date was approaching. After her retirement luncheon, she told the CEO that she and her husband were moving to Oklahoma. She asked if he would approve a check for the $25 delivery fee owed to her husband. The CEO signed the check request, she prepared a handwritten check accordingly, and the CEO signed it. After leaving the office for the last time, the bookkeeper made two stops that afternoon.

```
                                              6789

Pay to    Paper Clip Delivery Service          $25.00

The Sum  Twenty-five and no/100          Dollars


                          J. Johnson
```

First Stop, Her Company's Bank   At the bank, the bookkeeper went to the center island and removed the funds transfer slip from her purse. It was dated 3/17/yy. This day's date was August 17, so she simply changed the three to an eight, and she then transferred the $35,000 to the disbursing account.

Second Stop, Her Husband's Bank   She then drove to the bank where her husband's Paper Clip Delivery Service account was held. Unknown to anyone, when she had made out the handwritten check, she used erasable ink! She erased the amounts and then had in her hands a blank, signed check:

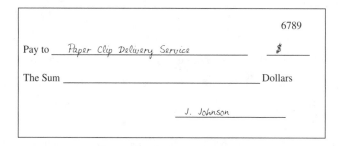

```
                                              6789

Pay to    Paper Clip Delivery Service          $

The Sum                                   Dollars


                          J. Johnson
```

Unbelievably, she marked the check up to $35,000!

```
                                              7894

Pay to    Paper Clip Delivery Service          $35,000.00

The Sum  Thirty-five thousand and no/100    Dollars


                          J. Johnson
```

She knew that the bank's cut-off date for bank statements was the 15th of the month. By doing the fraudulent transaction on the 17th, she knew that the altered check wouldn't be discovered for a month. She returned to the bank a week later, when the funds had been transferred and the altered check had cleared the banking system. She closed out the account and pocketed the $35,000.

Tip   If it is necessary to hand-write a check, always use a gel pen rather than an ink pen. Another common trick is to put tape over a check signature, dip the check in a common household liquid that erases all but the printer's ink, and then blow-dry the check. The thief now has a signed check with no payee or amounts. The solvent eradicates ink, but not gel.

The Case of the Petty Cash Fund

A trusted staff accountant was also the petty cash agent (not uncommon in most small businesses). At the end of each month, he typed up a check to himself for $100 to replenish the fund, and presented the check to the CEO for his signature.

```
                                                    7894

Pay to ___ Donald Miller _____        $100.00

The Sum _____ One hundred & no/100 _____ Dollars


                               E. Layden
```

After hours, alone in the office, the accountant put the check back into the typewriter and lined up the striker across from the number 1. He hit the backspace key and typed in a comma. He then hit the key twice and typed in a 0. And finally, he pressed it twice again and typed a 1, changing the numbered amount from $100.00 to $10,100.00. A hefty petty cash fund.

To complete the transaction, he lined up the striker across from the letter O, hit the backspace key the appropriate number of times, and typed in two words: Ten Thousand.

With that simple action, he was now in possession of a typed check, signed by the CEO, and payable to himself for $10,100.00.

```
                                                    7894

Pay to ___ Donald Millar _____       $10,100.00

The Sum __ Ten Thousand One hundred & no/100 ____ Dollars


                               E. Layden
```

He deposited the check in an out-of-state bank. He did this for ten consecutive months. Since the bank statements were mailed directly to him, he knew that no one would be aware of the altered checks, and he simply falsified the financial statements he prepared.

$101,000 richer, the accountant gave his notice just two weeks before the CPA firm was due in. The theft was discovered, but much too late.

Preventing Check Scams

The altering of the ten petty cash checks took place during the classic embezzler's window of opportunity. This is the time that management has to be alert to potential fraud.

Of course, this scam would have been discovered, or not even attempted, if the CEO reviewed bank statements and canceled checks, off-site. Positive Pay, too, would have prevented these two scams.

And finally, manual checks can be protected if the amounts on the checks are printed with a check protector machine, available at any office supply store. This simple machine imprints the words THE SUM and the dollar amount on the appropriate line in blue and red ink, and perforates the paper.

Auditing Receipts

It is very important to arrange for a thorough audit of an entire month's receipts to verify that the proper accounts have been credited. And this should be done at least once a year.

Let's assume that you institute an internal control practice that requires that your office manager, administrative assistant, or receptionist endorse all checks received, complete a deposit slip, and maintain a log of those checks (as an audit trail) before sending them to finance.

One deposit includes a $1,000 check payable to the company. The checks and deposit slips are sent to finance, which processes them and physically deposits them at the bank (including the $1,000 check), which clears the bank routinely.

Sounds fine, except that the finance director credited the $1,000 check to the Federal Income Tax Withheld account, instead of the proper one. The $1,000 is now considered withheld income tax on the finance director's personal return. At the end of the year, she simply adds the $1,000 to the actual amount withheld on her personal W-2. She has given herself a "bonus" of $1,000 in the form of a personal IRS income tax refund check.

The original check was never tampered with. It was simply credited to the Federal Income Tax Withheld account, instead of a revenue account. To prevent this type of embezzlement, you should arrange for a thorough audit of an entire month's receipts, to ensure that every check received has been credited to the proper account—especially, during the embezzler's window of opportunity, the time between one year's audit and the one in the following year.

Steps to Take If You Have Been Victimized by Fraud

Documenting a Fraud Action Plan

OBVIOUSLY, NO ONE wants to be the victim of a fraud scheme, but possible victimization is a reality all organizations face. A prudent business practice is to have a preplanned and well-thought-out strategy of action to take if fraud is suspected. A draft of such a plan follows:

1. **Never ever accuse anyone of an impropriety—get the facts.**

   Remember that you may be wrong, and if you are, there is a probability you will be on the wrong end of a defamation lawsuit. Be patient and thoroughly investigate the situation before any action is taken.

2. **Contact an employment law attorney.**

   If you suspect fraud, get advice on how to proceed, from a competent employment law attorney familiar with your state and federal employment law. This is a very important step in avoiding any associated legal issues concerning termination for fraud.

3. **Contact your independent CPA.**

   Inform your independent CPA firm that fraud is suspected and inquire if they are competent in the areas of fraud investigation, forensic accounting, and so forth. If they don't feel comfortable in this area, ask them to recommend a CPA firm that is experienced in this area.

   Once you have contacted the right CPA firm, they will assist you with the investigation, help with any insurance claims, prepare for going to trial if necessary, and handle other important areas suggested in this plan of action.

4. **Work from copies.**

   When you initially contact your independent CPA firm, they will tell you the importance of protecting the evidence and working from copies of original documents related to the incident.

   Place the original documents in a safe deposit box or safe location that the offender does not have access to. Remember that copies of documents are often not admissible as evidence in court, and if original documents are lost, stolen, or altered, a valuable aspect of your criminal case, insurance claims, and the like may be compromised.

5. **Take detailed, copious notes.**

   Again, when you initially contact your independent CPA, you will be told of the importance of taking detailed and thorough notes of everything related to the incident.

   Realistically, it may be *years* before going to trial after the incident is discovered, and anything can happen in the meantime: an understandable loss of memory, people retiring, people resigning, and so forth. When detailed notes are taken, a full record of the incident will be available to another employee, attorneys, CPAs, and the like.

6. **Read your Fidelity Bond!**

   After review, note important provisions of your bond in this plan of action, such as police report requirements, required time frame to file a claim with the insurance company, and so forth.

7. **Review the Conditions of Employment agreement.**

   This is always an uncomfortable situation, but the stress may be relieved somewhat if the employee was required to sign the important Conditions of Employment agreement whereby the employee has acknowledged that he or she understands what to expect in the event of a fraud investigation.

   Note: Please reference and read thoroughly "Conditions of Employment Agreement," in Section 3 of this manual.

   Steps 8 through 16 are concerned with actually confronting the alleged perpetrator and are included in the agreement.

8. **Do not discuss the situation in the employee's office, cubicle, or other work area.**

   Never have this discussion in the employee's office, but rather in an executive's office, conference room, library, or another neutral location. Remember that the offender's office almost assuredly contains vital evidence related to the incident.

Never allow an offender access to this evidence because it will be important to forensic accountants, attorneys, police detectives, insurance company, and so forth.

9. **Always have a witness.**

At a minimum, the termination discussion should *always* include a witness selected by management, regardless of the nature of the situation. This witness is of particular importance in the event of any form of male-versus-female confrontation. If a man finds it necessary to confront a woman, the witness should always be another woman. Conversely, if a woman has to confront a man, the witness should be another man.

Obviously, the purpose of the male/female confrontation witness is to avoid any allegations of sexual impropriety and for physical protection of the woman.

It's possible that other witnesses may be required, such as your attorney, CPA, or other persons essential to the case.

10. **Protect yourself and other employees.**

It is a sad commentary on our society, but realistically, violence in the workplace is common.

If there is even a *hint* that this is a possibility, contact your local police department for advice. Often they will either send a uniformed officer to sit in on the discussion or allow off-duty officers to provide this service for a fee. Regardless, the police department will be prepared to offer advice as to how to proceed.

11. **Change computer passwords!**

While the discussion is taking place, have an Information Technology (IT) representative void the suspect's computer passwords and address any other important IT issues such as email access and so forth. Failure to do this could result in the suspected offender's accessing the system off-site, compromising important data, and so forth.

12. **Have the discussion during nonbusiness hours.**

Ensure that the confrontation takes place before or after regular business hours. The purpose of this, of course, is to avoid an unnecessary office scene, embarrassment, and the like.

13. **Ensure surrender of organization property.**

The employee should be required to surrender organization property such as door keys, credit cards and so forth. It may also be necessary to have the locks changed.

14. **Employee should not collect his/her property from the office.**

    Have two employees go to the offender's office to remove important personal effects such as a purse, wallet, car keys, and the like. Two employees should always do this to avoid any accusations of theft of cash.

15. **Escort the perpetrator from the office.**

    Never allow the employee to return to his or her office—remember, the office contains valuable evidence important to the fraud investigation, forensic accountants, and attorneys, and if the employee has access to evidence it could affect the integrity of the case.

16. **Have other employee property gathered by coworkers.**

    Inform the offender that nonessential employee property such as photos will be gathered by two employees, and these items will be couriered to the employee's residence the following business day.

17. **Make notes of the discussion.**

    After the discussion, the executive and the witness should compile detailed notes of the discussion. The notes should include, at a minimum, the following:

    ➣ Date and time of the discussion
    ➣ Names and contact information of the executive, witness, police officers, CPA, attorney, and the like.
    ➣ The offender's physical reactions to questioning
    ➣ Other important information as needed

    The purpose of these notes is to provide detail needed by attorneys and accountants in the event that litigation is necessary.

18. **Get a police report, if necessary.**

    On advice of your attorney, don't neglect to file a police report of the incident, as this report is required of Fidelity Bond claims, forensic accounting data, litigation strategy, and so forth.

19. **Proceed with a Fidelity Bond claim.**

    It is very common for management to take the Fidelity Bond (employee dishonesty insurance) for granted and not know who is included on the bond, the amount of the bond, and actions to take to proceed with a claim.

20. **Prosecute?**

    The perpetrator should be aware that the organization (or the Fidelity Bond carrier) may prosecute the offender in the event of employee dishonesty.

The Conditions of Employment agreement should clearly state that prosecution may lead to a criminal record. Criminal records are public information and discoverable by subsequent employers pursuing background checks on prospective employees, significantly damaging the offender's prospects for employment.

Obviously, the discussion to prosecute would be made on a case-by-case basis, but material dishonesty should always be prosecuted. If there is no prosecution, there is no record, and the offender could perpetrate the scam on an unsuspecting subsequent employer.

21. **Decide how to relate the circumstances of dismissal to others.**

Get advice of counsel on how to handle relating circumstances of the termination:

➤ Internally with staff
➤ With inquiring customers and so forth
➤ With regard to reference checks by subsequent employers

22. **And when it's all over. . . .**

Reconstruct the details of the occurrence and change procedures so that it cannot happen again!

Fraud Examinations and Assembling the Fraud Team

A fraud examination is significantly different from an audit, although it is understandable that someone not familiar with the various services offered by a CPA could confuse the two.

An audit of financial statements is very general, and the purpose is for the CPA to express an opinion on the financial statements, hopefully unqualified. Exposing fraud is not the goal of an audit, although occasionally, of course, fraud is discovered during the course of a routine financial audit.

A fraud examination is usually very specific and due to suspicion that fraud may exist or have already occurred. It is very important to assume that a fraud examination will eventually end up in court, so it is essential that detailed and copious notes be prepared as the engagement progresses.

A typical fraud examination consists of the following steps:

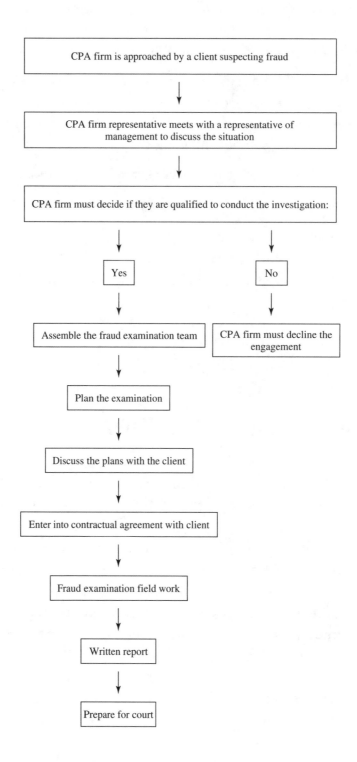

CPA Firm Approached by Client Suspecting Fraud

Typically, the client has already discovered fraud or is suspicious of an internal embezzlement or outside fraud, and their first impulse is to contact their CPA firm for help and guidance.

After this initial contact is made, a meeting should be arranged between representatives of the client and CPA firm.

CPA Firm/Client Meeting

This meeting should take place either at the CPA's office or a neutral location, but never at the client's office, if it is believed the fraud is ongoing, and suspected employees are still on staff.

At this meeting, a full discussion of the suspicious activity takes place, and the two parties reach a conclusion as to whether or not to proceed.

CPA Firm Qualified to Proceed?

The CPA firm representatives must examine their qualifications to proceed. If the fraud examination is beyond their abilities, they have an obligation to decline the engagement and advise the client that it would be in their best interest to select another firm.

Assuming that the CPA firm is satisfied with their qualifications to proceed, the next step would be to assemble the fraud examination team.

Fraud Examination Team

Of course, every fraud is different from the next, so the individuals serving on the team will vary from incident to incident. It is possible that one examination would only require the services of one experienced CPA, while another may be composed of several people.

Possible fraud examination team members may include the following:

➤ Members of the CPA firm
➤ CPAs from other firms experienced with fraud examination
➤ Labor law attorneys
➤ Criminal law attorneys
➤ Outside consultants
➤ Computer and software experts
➤ Private investigators
➤ Client representatives
➤ Others as deemed necessary

Planning the Examination

Once the fraud examination team is assembled, they work out the details of the fraud examination plan based on what is known at the time about the incident. Details, of course, may change once field work is commenced and more information becomes available.

Discussions with Management

The next logical step is for representatives of the CPA firm and management to meet, once again either at the CPA's office or a neutral location, to discuss the following:

- ➤ Initial fraud examination plan
- ➤ Roles and responsibilities of team members
- ➤ Time frames
- ➤ Financial arrangements
- ➤ Final written report
- ➤ Other areas particular to the incident

Contracting with the Client

Obviously, the CPA firm and client should enter into a contract detailing key elements of the fraud examination to avoid misunderstandings, particularly regarding financial arrangements.

Field Work

Depending upon the nature of the incident, elements of field work may vary. Typical field work may consist of the following:

- ➤ Cut-off bank statement or online review of cleared checks and the like
- ➤ Cut-off credit card statement review
- ➤ Collection of evidence
- ➤ Inquiries and interviews of key personnel, witnesses, and so forth
- ➤ Observations of behavior

Important: As noted, a key element of a fraud examination is the expectation that the incident may go to court. Therefore, adequate documentation of all actions taken, evidence collection, interview results, and so forth is absolutely essential.

Written Report

A written report will be prepared, summarizing the incident, backed up by details gathered during field work. Remember, never accuse anyone of any wrongdoing, and don't hesitate to secure appropriate legal opinion when necessary.

Preparing for Court

Preparing to go to trial dictates that a forensic accountant become involved. For a full discussion on the role of a forensic accountant and preparing for litigation, see "The Basics of Forensic Accounting," next.

In summary, a fraud examination is substantially different from an audit of the financial statements. This work is challenging, always different, and often very rewarding and satisfying, when an engagement is successful.

The Basics of Forensic Accounting

Technically, the term "forensic accounting" means preparing an expert witness accountant for litigation as part of a team representing either the prosecution or defense in a matter relating to a fraudulent activity. Over time, however, the term "forensic accounting" has also become synonymous with investigative accounting procedures. We will now address literal definitions of forensic accounting, that is preparing to go to court, and will explore the steps from selection of a forensic accountant to testimony.

Forensic Accountant vs. Traditional Accountant

As stated previously, a forensic accountant is one prepared to go to trial, while a traditional accountant is one recognized as an authority in the discipline of accounting. Practically all forensic accountants started their careers as traditional accountants in various roles such as bookkeepers, controllers, tax preparers, chief financial officers, independent CPAs, and so forth, because experience in traditional accounting fields is an important qualification for a forensic accountant.

Forensic accountants are commonly relied on in several areas, the most common being:

➤ Divorce settlements

➤ Business valuations

➤ Personal injury

➤ Embezzlement, fraud, identity theft, and falsification of financial statements

Here, we will address only the last bullet point, that being fraud issues.

Forensic Accounting: Education and Training

As stated previously, almost all practicing forensic accountants started their careers as traditional accountants, and therefore their basic educations routinely mirror each other. Basic education typically includes undergraduate study and postgraduate study, and almost all forensic accountants eventually become CPAs, because this credential is a vital component of the expert witness accountant's curriculum vitae, discussed below.

Typically, one desiring to make the transition from traditional accountant to forensic accountant would seek out and work for a CPA firm specializing in this field for invaluable hands-on experience.

Finally, this person typically would join professional organizations recognized in the fraud area, such as the Society of Certified Fraud Examiners, to take advantage of seminars offered on the subject and so forth.

Characteristics of Competent Forensic Accountants

Traditional accountants are often stereotyped as unassuming, conservative, detail-oriented, quiet, and well-educated professionals, and these stereotypes are generally found to be true. Although these traits clearly vary among individuals, a few of these traits would be detrimental to a forensic accountant.

The forensic accountant will be retained as an expert witness during deposition and litigation, and thus experience very tough questioning from opposing counsel in front of jurors. A good forensic accountant has to be thick-skinned and self-confident and have excellent verbal and written communication skills. In other words, a good forensic accountant is viewed as someone more extroverted than a typical traditional accountant.

Building a Curriculum Vitae

Before selecting the expert witness forensic accountant, an attorney will request a curriculum vitae (CV) from each candidate considered. Obviously, the CV that includes better education, experience, professional credentials, articles authored, professional affiliations, and so forth will be given more consideration, so plan to firm it up.

A typical CV includes the following:

➤ Personal information such as name, address, telephone number, email address, and so on
➤ Degrees earned
➤ Professional credentials (Certified Public Accountants (CPA), Certified Fraud Examiner (CFE), etc.)
➤ Continuing professional education
➤ Professional memberships American Institute of Certified Public Accountants (AICPA), state societies of CPAs, American Society of Certified Fraud Examiners (ASCFE), etc.)
➤ Prior expert witness experience
➤ Books and articles authored
➤ Military history
➤ Employment history

The CV should be thorough, but there is a fine line that separates thoroughness from *too* much information, because opposing counsel will try to exploit any weaknesses included. The attorney will give advice on what to include or not include before the CV is provided to opposing counsel.

Finally, ensure that all information included in the CV is truthful and factual, because any erroneous statements will be a major embarrassment and possibly affect the outcome of the trial if discovered by opposing counsel.

Tip: An individual intimidated by speaking in public would not project the air of self-confidence required of a testifying forensic accountant. If that is the case, consider taking public speaking training such as a Dale Carnegie course. Also offer to speak on the subject for your local chamber of commerce or church. In addition to valuable speaking practice, these engagements can legitimately be included on your CV.

Another Tip: Having articles published is an essential aspect of a strong CV, because it establishes the forensic accountant as an expert in the field. Getting an article published isn't nearly as difficult as you might imagine.

➤ First, draft an article on some interesting embezzlement you were involved in uncovering or became aware of.

➤ Second, have your article edited. Rarely can anyone edit his or her own work, and an article that is not professional will not likely be considered for publication.

➤ Third, do your homework. Remember, magazines, newsletters, and newspapers are *looking* for content! Submit your article first to the editor of a local publication that you feel may be interested in your work, and work your way up to larger publications. You'll be surprised how often your work is accepted!

Personal Attributes

The rules of discovery mandate that the CV of the forensic accountant be provided to opposing counsel, so, as stated earlier, it is imperative that all information be truthful. It is equally important that the forensic accountant have high standards of personal integrity and remain cool under pressure from the opposition's lawyer.

In addition to professional information included in the CV, opposing counsel will also investigate the *personal* background of the forensic accountant to discredit his or her testimony during litigation.

Personal information that may be brought up at trial may include:

➤ Academic grades

➤ Current status of license and any lapses

➤ Current status of compliance with Continuing Professional Education requirements

➤ Driving record issues such as a DWI or DUI

➤ Criminal record

➤ Credit record

➤ Employment history

➤ Divorce issues

➤ Substance abuse issues

➤ Bankruptcy

➤ Lawsuits

- Liens
- Questionable business associates or friends
- Relationship with the client or client's associates
- Relationship with the client's attorney
- Conflicts of interest
- Fee arrangements

If a forensic accountant has anything embarrassing in his or her past, it is important that he or she advise the attorney he or she is working with. No one is expecting the forensic accountant to be perfect—just be prepared that it is likely these items may come up at the trial, and get advice from your lawyer about how to respond on the witness stand if they do.

The Team

A typical forensic accounting engagement involves, at a minimum, a team of three:

- The attorney
- The forensic accountant
- Another accountant who will assist the attorney and work behind the scenes

Roles:

Attorney: Obviously, the attorney represents his or her client, plans case strategy, and works with the forensic accountant and accounting assistant.

Forensic Accountant: He or she will eventually appear in court as an expert witness. Remember, the forensic accountant's CV is open to discovery; this person must be cool under pressure from questioning by opposing counsel and is under oath.

Accounting Assistant: This person's background is generally *not* subject to the discovery rules. Therefore, this person typically does the on-site detail work and acts as a technical advisor to the attorney.

The Agreement

To avoid any possible misunderstandings, often the attorney may want a letter of agreement from the forensic accountant. Typically, this agreement includes the following:

- Fee arrangement
- Scope of work to be performed
- Anything unique or important relating to the engagement
- Deadlines

Sample Accounting Firm/Attorney Agreement Letter

Date_____

Attorney Name
Firm Name
Street Address
City, State, Zip Code

Dear_____:

This letter is to confirm our conversation with regard to providing forensic accounting services with regard to (case).

Fees for services provided and related expenses will be billed as follows:

Expert Witness: $_____ per hour
Services to be provided:
     Conferences
     Depositions
     Testimony
     Other services as necessary

Senior Accounting Staff: $_____per hour
Services to be provided:
     Conferences
     Data examinations
     Report preparation (if requested)
     Other services as necessary

Clerical Staff: $_____per hour

Expenses:
     Travel
     Photocopying
     Postage/Courier
     Other expenses as necessary

If the terms of this arrangement are acceptable, please sign on the appropriate line, date and return with a retainer fee of $_____.

Sincerely,

Accountant Name
Firm Name

Agreed:

_____
Attorney Name

_____
Date

Field Work

Field work is the actual investigation and information-gathering portion of the incident in preparation for going to trial. A good guideline to consider when planning field work is the requirements included in SAS 99, "Consideration of Fraud in a Financial Statement Audit," (Section 2 of this book) as well as elements included in a fraud audit.

Important elements to consider include:

1. Protection of evidence

   When evidence such as tampered checks, deposit slips, bank statements, and the like are gathered, it is very important to remember to safeguard the original document by placing it in a safe deposit box or other secured location and *work from copies*. Why? It is possible that the document could be lost or stolen, and often copies are not allowed to be submitted as evidence, seriously jeopardizing the case. Safeguarding the evidence also prevents tampering with original documents.

2. Document, document, document!

   Take detailed and copious notes of *everything* related to the investigation, such as:

   ➤ Dates
   ➤ Times
   ➤ Actions taken
   ➤ Discussions held
   ➤ How physical evidence was gathered
   ➤ People interviewed
   ➤ Places visited
   ➤ Observations such as strange behavior
   ➤ Audit trails
   ➤ Witnesses

   The importance of adequate documentation cannot be overstated. Besides its obvious importance as evidence at the trial, this detailed documentation would be available and invaluable to a successor forensic accountant in the event that something happened to the original team. Additionally, it can often be *years* between the time field work is concluded and actually going to trial, and it would be understandable to forget details over an extended period of time.

Depositions

After the forensic accountant has been selected, the team gathered, and field work completed, the next phase of the assignment is preparing the forensic accountant for his or her deposition by opposing counsel.

A few points to remember:

➤ The opposing counsel is representing *his or her* client and therefore will do everything in their power to discredit the forensic accountant! Expect it and don't get upset—that's their job.

➤ Be prepared and review deposition strategy with your attorney.

➤ Remember, as noted earlier, it is likely that anything embarrassing about your past will come out during the deposition. Be prepared to respond appropriately as advised by the attorney.

➤ Be honest with your responses, and if you do not know the answer to a question, say so.

➤ The deposition will be in front of a court reporter. The court reporter will forward the written deposition to your lawyer. It is very important to review the written deposition carefully and bring any errors to the attention of your attorney for correction.

The Trial Phase

Okay, everyone has done his or her work to this point, and now we are preparing for the actual testimony of the forensic accountant as the expert witness at the trial.

Your attorney will review the following with you, but this is what you can expect to do:

1. Review all of the data so that you will be prepared.

2. Carefully review the written deposition so that you will not contradict yourself.

3. Discuss testimony strategy with your counsel.

4. Arrive early on the day of the trial.

5. Dress conservatively.

6. Pause before answering questions. Besides giving you more time to think, it allows your attorney time to object.

7. Don't speak to or even make eye contact with jurors.

8. Try to disassociate yourself from questioning, and don't take the questions personally. Remember, you are not on trial.

The Pros and Cons of Forensic Accounting

Pros:

1. **It's emotionally rewarding.**

   It's a nice feeling to know that you are contributing something positive to society by exposing fraud and corruption and helping to protect victimized and innocent people.

2. **It is exciting, challenging, and varied.**

Each individual incident of embezzlement is almost always different from the others, and thus piecing together parts of a complex scenario is usually challenging—requiring thoroughness and ingenuity—but very satisfying when a conclusion is reached.

3. **It can be lucrative.**

Individuals hire forensic accountants because of their experience and, like specialists in any other field, forensic accountants can expect compensation that can be very lucrative.

Cons:

1. **Failure.**

On occasion, people perpetrating fraud are so clever and cunning that coming to a satisfactory conclusion of an investigation is virtually impossible. This of course is very frustrating.

2. **Working within the system.**

Another downside to forensic accounting is accepting the fact that often the dragon slays the knight, or in other words, the perpetrator "beats the system."

It is always frustrating to prove conclusively that an embezzlement took place, only to see the case dismissed due to a technicality.

3. **Opposing attorneys.**

If an engagement goes to court, the forensic accountant will have to face the opposing counsel in both the deposition and testimony phases.

As stated earlier, it is that attorney's job to protect his or her client, and therefore the attorney will do all he or she can to discredit the expert witness not only regarding professional qualifications, but also very personal issues that may be embarrassing. It is difficult not to take these statements personally.

4. **Intimidation.**

Unfortunately, violence in the workplace is a fact of life in our society. While rare, intimidation of a forensic accountant has happened. Remember, desperate people can take desperate action, and take whatever action you deem necessary to protect yourself.

Tip: When planning your career, consider having business cards, letterhead, and the like with a post office address rather than a street address. Why? For the protection of everyone, it may be better that your office address or residence not be known to certain unsavory individuals.

Internal Control Analysis, Documentation, and Recommendations for Improvement

Internal Control Analysis, Documentation, and Recommendations for Improvement

THE INFORMATION ABOUT internal control analysis and documentation that follows is a resource and guide for independent CPAs, internal auditors, and an organization's staff, for analyzing the entity's system of internal controls, exposing risks and considering recommendations for improvement.

Obviously, this tool is not designed as a perfect fit for every entity, and thus several situations will not apply to very small organizations, and other areas not included will have to be considered for very large entities.

The analysis that follows addresses internal control issues in the following areas:

➤ Financial and accounting administration

➤ Risk assessment and understanding the entity

➤ Brainstorming sessions/employee interviews

➤ Bank and credit card statements

➤ Payroll

➤ Receipts and accounts receivable

➤ Disbursements and accounts payable

➤ Inventory

➤ Fixed assets, depreciation, and amortization

➤ Travel expenses

➤ Postage and shipping

➤ Fidelity Bonds
➤ Gift offers
➤ Cash, cash equivalents, and investments
➤ Implementing an embezzlement and fraud action plan

Internal Control Analysis, Documentation, and Recommendations for Improvement

Organization _____

In-Charge Accountant _____

Accounting Assistants _____

_____

_____

_____

_____

Financial and Accounting Administration

➤ List the names of officers and employees in the following positions:

Position	Name
Treasurer	_____
Chief Financial Officer	_____
Controller	_____
Senior Accountant(s)	_____
	_____
	_____
General Ledger Accountant(s)	_____
	_____
	_____
Payroll Supervisor	_____
Payroll Clerks	_____
	_____
	_____
Accounts Payable Supervisor	_____
Accounts Payable Clerks	_____
	_____
	_____
Accounts Receivable Supervisor	_____
Accounts Receivable Clerks	_____
	_____
	_____

Others:

_____	_____
_____	_____
_____	_____

➤ List names and titles of all check signers:

Name	Title
_____	_____
_____	_____
_____	_____
_____	_____
_____	_____

➤ As a supplement to this internal control evaluation and audit work papers, have a member of the audit team witness the authorized check signers recording their original signatures as they would sign checks. Random checks should be compared to original signatures for authenticity.

<u>Name</u>   <u>Signature</u>

_____   _____

_____   _____

_____   _____

_____   _____

_____   _____

Witness name   _____

Witness signature   _____

Date _____

➤ Note the title and names of employees who prepare the bank deposit:

<u>Title</u>   <u>Name</u>

_____   _____

_____   _____

_____   _____

➤ Are controls surrounding the preparation of   Yes   No
bank deposits adequate?   ____   ____

If no, explain and record recommendations for improvement, if applicable:

_____

_____

_____

_____

_____

➤ Note how funds are physically deposited into the bank:

_____

_____

_____

_____

_____

➤ Note names and titles of employees who are responsible for making bank deposits:

Name	Title
_____	_____
_____	_____
_____	_____

➤ Are controls surrounding depositing receipts   Yes   No
and employee safety adequate?   ____   ____

If no, explain and record recommendations for improvement, if applicable:

_____

_____

_____

_____

_____

➤ List the names and titles of employees responsible for reconciling bank statements:

Name	Title
_____	_____
_____	_____
_____	_____

➤ Are all bank statements reconciled   Yes   No
monthly and promptly?   ____   ____

If no, explain and record recommendations for improvement, if applicable:

_____

_____

_____

_____

_____

➤ Are copies of bank reconciliations attached
to monthly internal financial statements?

Yes	No
____	____

If no, detail that it has been explained to management that this is a recommended procedure to reduce embezzlement through manipulation of bank statement reconciliations:

_____

_____

_____

_____

_____

➤ Are the individuals responsible for
reconciling bank statements different from
those responsible for check preparation?

Yes	No	N/A
____	____	____

If no, explain and record recommendations for improvement, if applicable:

_____

_____

_____

_____

_____

➤ List names and titles of employees who prepare disbursement checks:

Name	Title
_____	_____
_____	_____
_____	_____

➤ List names and titles of employees recording accounts receivables and general receipts:

Name	Title
_____	_____
_____	_____
_____	_____

➤ List names and titles of employees who open and distribute mail:

Name   Title

_____   _____

_____   _____

_____   _____

➤ Describe journal entry preparation and approval procedures:

_____

_____

_____

_____

_____

➤ Are full explanations required for all   Yes   No
  journal entries?   ____   ____

If no, explain and record recommendations for improvement, if applicable:

_____

_____

_____

_____

_____

➤ List names and titles of employees authorized to prepare journal entries:

Name   Title

_____   _____

_____   _____

_____   _____

➤ List names and titles of employees responsible for reviewing and approving journal entries:

Name   Title

_____   _____

_____   _____

_____   _____

➤ Are procedures surrounding reviewing and   Yes   No
approving journal entries adequate?   ____   ____

If no, explain and record recommendations for improvement, if applicable:

_____

_____

_____

_____

_____

➤ List the names and titles of petty cash agents:

<u>Name</u>   <u>Title</u>

_____   _____

_____   _____

_____   _____

➤ What is the amount of the petty cash fund? $_____

➤ Is the amount of the petty cash fund   Yes   No   N/A
reasonable under the circumstances?   ____   ____   ____

If no, explain and record recommendations for improvement, if applicable:

_____

_____

_____

_____

_____

➤ Describe petty cash disbursement procedures:

_____

_____

_____

_____

_____

➤ Are procedures surrounding petty cash fund   Yes   No
    disbursements and security adequate?   ____   ____

If no, explain and record recommendations for improvement, if applicable:

_____

_____

_____

_____

_____

➤ Are there adequate job descriptions for   Yes   No
    all accounting positions?   ____   ____

If no, explain and record recommendations for improvement, if applicable:

_____

_____

_____

_____

_____

➤ Does the organization have an Accounting
    and Financial Policies and Procedures Manual,   Yes   No
    and is the manual current and thorough?   ____   ____

If no, explain and record recommendations for improvement, if applicable:

_____

_____

_____

_____

➤ When employees assigned to finance
    are on vacation, does another employee   Yes   No
    assume their responsibilities?   ____   ____

If no, explain and record recommendations for improvement, if applicable:

_____

_____

_____

_____

_____

➤ Have all accounting personnel signed   Yes   No
   a Conflict of Interest agreement?   _____   _____

   If no, explain and record recommendations for improvement, if applicable:

   _____

   _____

   _____

   _____

   _____

➤ Have all accounting personnel signed   Yes   No
   a Conditions of Employment agreement?   _____   _____

   If no, explain and record recommendations for improvement, if applicable:

   _____

   _____

   _____

   _____

   _____

➤ Is the chart of accounts current   Yes   No
   and thorough?   _____   _____

   If no, explain and record recommendations for improvement, if applicable:

   _____

   _____

   _____

   _____

   _____

➤ Are old charts of account retained for   Yes   No
   audit purposes?   _____   _____

If no, explain and record recommendations for improvement, if applicable:

_____

_____

_____

_____

_____

	Yes	No
➤ Does the organization require thorough background checks for all finance personnel and other key positions?	____	____

If no, explain and record recommendations for improvement, if applicable:

_____

_____

_____

_____

_____

	Yes	No
➤ Do background checks include the following?		
➤ Criminal history	____	____
➤ Credit check	____	____
➤ Driver's license record	____	____
➤ Education credentials	____	____
➤ Professional credentials	____	____
➤ Prior employment verification	____	____
➤ Reference check	____	____
➤ Social Security number verification	____	____
➤ Drug testing	____	____
➤ FBI fingerprint check	____	____

Other items included in background checks:

➤ _____

➤ _____

➤ _____

➤ _____

If background checks are not adequate, explain and record recommendations for improvement, if applicable:

_____

_____

_____

_____

_____

➤ Does the organization have an Internal   Yes   No
Control Policies and Procedures Handbook?   ____   ____

If no, explain and record recommendations for improvement, if applicable:

_____

_____

_____

_____

_____

➤ Is there a written policy whereby
employees are required to report
suspicious activities, conflicts of interest,
or unethical behavior to the appropriate   Yes   No
level of management?   ____   ____

If no, explain and record recommendations for improvement, if applicable:

_____

_____

_____

_____

_____

➤ Does the organization have a whistleblower
protection policy prohibiting retaliation   Yes   No
against whistleblowers?   ____   ____

If no, explain and record recommendations for improvement, if applicable:

_____

_____

_____

_____

_____

➤ Does the organization have a policy
whereby terminated employees are subject   Yes   No
to an exit interview?
                                                  ____   ____

If no, explain and record recommendations for improvement, if applicable:

_____

_____

_____

_____

_____

➤ Does the exit interview include the following questions?

   ➤ Are you aware of any existing illegal
   activity, conflicts of interest,   Yes   No
   or unethical conduct?
                                                 ____   ____

   ➤ Are you aware of any potential
   illegal activity, conflicts of interest,
   or unethical conduct?   ____   ____

   ➤ Have you ever been approached by
   anyone to join him or her in an illegal act? ____   ____

   ➤ Are there any lapses in existing internal
   controls that you are uncomfortable with?   ____   ____

Note other exit interview questions:

   ➤ _____

   _____

   _____

   ➤ _____

   _____

   _____

   ➤ _____

   _____

   _____

➤ If the answers to any exit interview
questions are cause for concern, is the   Yes   No
appropriate level of management advised?   ____   ____

If no, explain and record recommendations for improvement, if applicable:

_____

_____

_____

_____

_____

➤ Is the exit interview conducted by someone
not in the employee's direct line of   Yes   No
employment responsibility?   ____   ____

If no, explain and record recommendations for improvement, if applicable:

_____

_____

_____

_____

_____

➤ Does the organization have an Insurance
Committee to ensure that all insurance   Yes   No
policies are adequate?   ____   ____

If no, explain and record recommendations for improvement, if applicable:

_____

_____

_____

_____

_____

➤ Does the organization have an Internal   Yes   No   N/A
Audit Committee?   ____   ____   ____

If no, explain and record recommendations for improvement, if applicable:

_____

_____

_____

_____

_____

➤ Are the functions of the Internal
  Audit Committee documented in an
  Internal Audit Committee Policies and   Yes   No   N/A
  Procedures Handbook?   ____   ____   ____

If no, explain and record recommendations for improvement, if applicable:

_____

_____

_____

_____

_____

➤ Does the organization have a code of ethics   Yes   No   N/A
  for financial management?   ____   ____   ____

If no, explain and record recommendations for improvement, if applicable:

_____

_____

_____

_____

_____

➤ Does the organization issue a Financial   Yes   No   N/A
  Statement Certification?   ____   ____   ____

If no, explain and record recommendations for improvement, if applicable:

_____

_____

_____

_____

_____

➤ If the organization does issue a Financial Statement Certification, note titles and names of signers:

Title	Name
_____	_____
_____	_____
_____	_____
_____	_____
_____	_____

➤ Are controls over wire transfers and other electronic payments adequate?

Yes   No   N/A

____   ____   ____

If no, explain and record recommendations for improvement, if applicable:

_____

_____

_____

_____

_____

➤ Has the bank been made aware that any changes regarding authorized signatures on check signature cards, wire transfer contracts, activations on lines of credit, and loans require the approval of the appropriate level of management?

Yes   No

____   ____

If no, explain and record recommendations for improvement, if applicable:

_____

_____

_____

_____

_____

➤ Does the organization require all individuals working in accounting to take a full, uninterrupted week of vacation per year?

Yes   No

____   ____

If no, explain and record recommendations for improvement, if applicable:

_____

_____

_____

_____

_____

➤ Are all accounting employees subject to an
unanticipated day off work, and does another   Yes   No
employee assume their responsibilities?   ____   ____

If no, explain and record recommendations for improvement, if applicable:

_____

_____

_____

_____

_____

Comment on any specific financial and accounting administration issues that
indicate that the system and controls are not adequate, with recommendations for
improvement.

_____

_____

_____

_____

_____

_____

Elected Leadership

Note the names and contact information of the organization's Executive Committee if applicable:

Chief Elected Officer:

Title	Name	Contact Information
_____	_____	_____
		_____
		_____
		_____

Treasurer:

Name	Contact Information
_____	_____
	_____
	_____
	_____

Corporate Secretary:

Name	Contact Information
_____	_____
	_____
	_____
	_____

Other Executive Committee members:

Title	Name	Contact Information
_____	_____	_____
		_____
		_____
		_____
_____	_____	_____
		_____
		_____
		_____
_____	_____	_____
		_____
		_____
		_____
_____	_____	_____
		_____
		_____
		_____
_____	_____	_____
		_____
		_____
		_____
_____	_____	_____
		_____
		_____
		_____

Note titles and names of other board of directors members:

Title	Name	Contact Information
_____	_____	_____
		_____
		_____
		_____
_____	_____	_____
		_____
		_____
		_____
_____	_____	_____
		_____
		_____
_____	_____	_____
		_____
		_____
		_____
_____	_____	_____
		_____
		_____
		_____
_____	_____	_____
		_____
		_____
		_____

Note the contact information for the current Budget and Finance Committee if applicable:

Chairman:

Name	Contact Information
_____	_____
	_____
	_____
	_____

Committee Members:

Name	Contact Information
_____	_____
	_____
	_____
	_____
_____	_____
	_____
	_____
	_____
_____	_____
	_____
	_____
	_____
_____	_____
	_____
	_____
	_____

Note the contact information for the Internal Audit Committee if applicable:

Chairman:

Name	Contact Information
_____	_____
	_____
	_____
	_____

Committee Members:

Name	Contact Information
_____	_____
	_____
	_____
	_____
_____	_____
	_____
	_____
	_____
_____	_____
	_____
	_____
	_____
_____	_____
	_____
	_____
	_____

Are there any other committees or individuals among the membership that have financial responsibilities, such as an investment committee, insurance committee, long-range planning committee, or the like?

Yes   No
_____   _____

If yes, note detail and contact information:

_____
_____
_____
_____
_____
_____
_____
_____
_____
_____
_____
_____
_____
_____
_____
_____
_____
_____
_____
_____
_____
_____
_____
_____
_____
_____
_____
_____
_____
_____
_____

Risk Assessment and Understanding the Entity

➤ List resources available and reviewed to assess if any of the organization's line item expenses are out of line with those of similar organizations:

_____

_____

_____

_____

_____

➤ If any line items were determined to be out of line, what analytical action was taken to determine if fraud might be present?

_____

_____

_____

_____

_____

Comment on any risk assessment issue that indicates that more study is required, and record recommendations for improvement:

_____

_____

_____

_____

_____

Brainstorming Sessions/Employee Interviews

SAS 99 requires CPA audit team members to meet and brainstorm concerning client fraud risk and internal control weaknesses, to decide what client employees to interview, and to choose interview questions. While not required, this practice should be considered by internal audit committees, etc.

➤ Names and titles of brainstorming committee members:

Name	Title
_____	_____
_____	_____
_____	_____
_____	_____

➤ Date of meeting _____

➤ Summarize all perceived internal control weaknesses discussed, and record recommendations for improvement:

_____

_____

_____

_____

_____

➤ Names and titles of employees to be interviewed:

Name	Title
_____	_____
_____	_____
_____	_____
_____	_____

➤ Specific interview questions:

  ➤ Is the organization's Conflict of Interest policy clear and understandable?

  ➤ Is the organization's Conditions of Employment agreement clear and understandable?

  ➤ Are you aware of the existence of fraud, conflicts of interest, or unethical behavior?

➤ Are you aware of any potential for fraud, conflicts of interest, or unethical behavior?

➤ Has any employee ever approached you to conspire in fraud, conflicts of interest, or unethical behavior?

➤ Has anyone outside the organization ever approached you to conspire in fraud, conflicts of interest, or unethical behavior?

➤ Are you aware of any weaknesses in internal controls that could lead to fraud?

➤ Are the controls over confidential customer information (credit card numbers, bank account numbers, etc.) adequate?

➤ Are controls over confidential employee personnel records adequate?

➤ Is the organization policy for reporting suspicious behavior to the appropriate level of management clear and understandable?

➤ Is the organization's whistleblower protection policy clear and understandable?

➤ Do you have any suggestions for improvement for the organization taken as a whole?

Other questions as determined by the committee:

_____

_____

_____

_____

_____

Results of Interviews:

The staff interviews and results should be written and included with the audit work papers.

After the interviews, the results should be discussed among audit team members who have the responsibility of analyzing the risks and formulating a plan of action.

➤ Note specific areas of concern resulting from staff interviews:

_____

_____

_____

_____

_____

➤ Detail the plan of action formulated to investigate areas of concern:

_____

_____

_____

_____

_____

➤ Summarize results of implementing the plan of action and further action warranted, if necessary:

_____

_____

_____

_____

_____

Comment on any brainstorming session or employee interview issues that need addressing, and record recommendations for improvement:

_____

_____

_____

_____

_____

Bank and Credit Card Statements

➤ Are the original bank statements sent
directly to the organization's finance
department by the issuer for review?

Yes   No

____   ____

If no, explain and record recommendations for improvement, if applicable:

_____

_____

_____

_____

_____

➤ List titles and names of employees responsible for reconciling bank statements,
next to the account(s) they are responsible for:

Title	Name	Bank Account(s)
_____	_____	_____
_____	_____	_____
_____	_____	_____
_____	_____	_____

➤ Are material checks that are noted as
outstanding on the prior year-end bank
statement reconciliations investigated
thoroughly (endorsement comparisons,
double payments, etc.) by either a member
of the CPA firm or Internal Audit Committee
before the start of the following year's audit?

Yes   No

____   ____

If no, explain and record recommendations for improvement, if applicable:

_____

_____

_____

_____

_____

➤ Are *copies* of bank statements mailed
  by the issuer to a secured post office box
  accessible only by the following?   Yes   No

   ➤ The CEO   _____   _____

   ➤ The treasurer   _____   _____

   ➤ Members of the Internal Audit Committee   _____   _____

If no, explain and record recommendations for improvement, if applicable:

_____

_____

_____

_____

_____

➤ Does the CEO, treasurer, or members of the
  Internal Audit Committee examine the fronts
  and backs of checks (either original checks,
  copies, or online images) and investigate: Yes   No

   ➤ Signature authenticity   _____   _____

   ➤ Out-of-sequence check numbers   _____   _____

   ➤ New vendors   _____   _____

   ➤ Unusual or large amounts   _____   _____

   ➤ Unusual endorsement stamps   _____   _____

If no, explain and record recommendations for improvement, if applicable:

_____

_____

_____

_____

_____

➤ Note all employees who have been issued credit cards: <u>N/A</u>

Name	Title	Card Type	Account No. (Last 4 Digits)	Card Maximum
_____	_____	_____	_____	$ _____
_____	_____	_____	_____	_____
_____	_____	_____	_____	_____
_____	_____	_____	_____	_____

➤ Are original credit card statements mailed
directly to the organization's finance
department for review and processing?

        Yes   No   N/A

        ____   ____   ____

If no, explain and record recommendations for improvement, if applicable:

_____

_____

_____

_____

➤ Describe the process for approving credit card transactions for payment:

                                         N/A

_____

_____

_____

_____

➤ Are the controls surrounding the approval
of credit card transactions adequate under
the circumstances?

        Yes   No   N/A

        ____   ____   ____

If no, explain and record recommendations for improvement, if applicable:

_____

_____

_____

_____

➤ Are *copies* of credit card statements mailed
by the issuer to a secured post office box
accessible only by the following?   Yes   No   N/A

   ➤ The CEO   ____   ____   ____

   ➤ The treasurer   ____   ____

   ➤ Members of the Internal Audit Committee   ____   ____

If no, explain and record recommendations for improvement, if applicable:

_____

_____

_____

_____

_____

➤ Do the CEO, treasurer or members
of the Internal Audit Committee examine
employee credit card statements and   Yes   No   N/A
investigate any suspicious transactions?   ____   ____   ____

If no, explain and record recommendations for improvement, if applicable:

_____

_____

_____

_____

_____

➤ Are employees who have been issued
organization credit cards aware of immediate   Yes   No   N/A
steps to take to report lost or stolen cards?   ____   ____   ____

If no, explain and record recommendations for improvement, if applicable:

_____

_____

_____

_____

_____

➤ If the organization reimburses employees
for purchases made on behalf of the   Yes   No   N/A
organization, are controls adequate?   ____   ____   ____

If no, explain and record recommendations for improvement, if applicable:

_____

_____

_____

_____

_____

Comment on any specific bank statement or credit card statement issues that indicate controls are not adequate, with recommendations for improvement:

_____

_____

_____

_____

_____

Payroll

➤ Record titles and names of payroll-processing personnel:

Title	Name
_____	_____
_____	_____
_____	_____
_____	_____

➤ Are procedures for adding new employees   Yes   No
  to the payroll adequate?   ____   ____

  If no, explain and record recommendations for improvement, if applicable:

  _____

  _____

  _____

  _____

  _____

➤ Are a minimum of two people involved   Yes   No   N/A
  in adding new employees to the payroll?   ____   ____   ____

  If no, explain and record recommendations for improvement, if applicable:

  _____

  _____

  _____

  _____

  _____

➤ Are a minimum of two people involved
  in processing payroll, and are they
  required to sign their signatures attesting   Yes   No   N/A
  that payroll is accurate?   ____   ____   ____

  If no, explain and record recommendations for improvement, if applicable:

  _____

  _____

_____

_____

_____

➤ Are two signatures required on all   Yes   No   N/A
   payroll checks?   ____   ____   ____

If no, explain and record recommendations for improvement, if applicable:

_____

_____

_____

_____

_____

➤ Are payroll checks signed by individuals   Yes   No   N/A
   not involved in processing payroll?   ____   ____   ____

If no, explain and record recommendations for improvement, if applicable:

_____

_____

_____

_____

_____

➤ If an outside payroll preparation service   Yes   No   N/A
   is used, are controls and reviews adequate? ____   ____   ____

If no, explain and record recommendations for improvement, if applicable:

_____

_____

_____

_____

_____

➤ If a payroll service is used, note the following:

Name of service _____

Address _____

_____

Contact Name _____

Telephone _____

➤ Is there a random check on payroll during
the year to ensure that wages are accurate   Yes   No
and that there are no ghosts on the payroll?   ____   ____

If no, explain and record recommendations for improvement, if applicable:

_____

_____

_____

_____

_____

➤ Is there a random check on a federal
tax deposit during the year to ensure that   Yes   No
it is accurate?   ____   ____

If no, explain and record recommendations for improvement, if applicable:

_____

_____

_____

_____

_____

➤ Is there a random check on state or
local tax deposit during the year to   Yes   No   N/A
ensure that they are accurate?   ____   ____   ____

If no, explain and record recommendations for improvement, if applicable:

_____

_____

_____

_____

_____

➤ Is the payroll account reconciled promptly
at the end of each month by someone not   Yes   No   N/A
involved in processing payroll?   ____   ____   ____

If no, explain and record recommendations for improvement, if applicable:

_____

_____

_____

_____

_____

➤ Are payroll checks or direct deposit receipts
distributed to employees by employees   Yes   No   N/A
not involved in processing payroll?   ____   ____   ____

If no, explain and record recommendations for improvement, if applicable:

_____

_____

_____

_____

_____

➤ Does the organization use time sheets
for employees covered by the Fair Labor
Standards Act (FLSA), and are they signed
by the employee and approved by the   Yes   No   N/A
employee's direct supervisor?   ____   ____   ____

If no, explain and record recommendations for improvement, if applicable:

_____

_____

_____

_____

_____

➤ If payroll checks are issued, does anyone monitor where they are being cashed?

    Yes ____   No ____

Note: Employees who do not deposit checks into bank accounts (expensive check cashing services, liquor stores, endorsing checks over to third parties, etc.) may be ghosts or may have financial difficulties.

If no, explain and record recommendations for improvement, if applicable:

_____

_____

_____

_____

_____

➤ If employee loans or advances are permitted, are controls, procedures, and approvals adequate?

    Yes ____   No ____   N/A ____

If no, explain and record recommendations for improvement, if applicable:

_____

_____

_____

_____

_____

➤ Are employee loans or advances balanced to the general ledger?

    Yes ____   No ____   N/A ____

If no, explain and record recommendations for improvement, if applicable:

_____

_____

_____

_____

_____

➤ Are any employee loans unusually large,   Yes   No   N/A
old, or unusual?   ____   ____   ____

If yes, explain and record recommendations for improvement, if applicable:

_____

_____

_____

_____

_____

➤ Do any employees have unusually large
numbers of dependents listed on their   Yes   No
W-4s, and are these validated as accurate?   ____   ____

If yes, explain and record recommendations for improvement, if applicable:

_____

_____

_____

_____

_____

Comment on any specific payroll-processing issues that indicate that controls are
not adequate, with recommendations for improvement:

_____

_____

_____

_____

_____

_____

_____

Receipts and Accounts Receivable

➤ Does the organization utilize a bank's
Lockbox Service for receipts that come   Yes   No   N/A
through the mail?   ____   ____   ____

If no, explain and record recommendations for improvement, if applicable:

_____

_____

_____

_____

_____

➤ If the organization does receive receipts
through the mail, has the advantage of using
a bank's Lockbox Service been explained   Yes   No   N/A
to the appropriate level of management?   ____   ____   ____

Note details accordingly:

_____

_____

_____

_____

_____

➤ If the organization is widely known by
its acronym, does it encourage vendors,
customers, members, etc., to make checks
payable to the full legal name of the   Yes   No   N/A
organization?   ____   ____   ____

If no, explain and record recommendations for improvement, if applicable:

_____

_____

_____

_____

_____

➤ Does the organization occasionally use a "secret shopper" to make purchases at the point of sale via cash, check, or credit card?

Yes   No   N/A

____   ____   ____

If no, explain and record recommendations for improvement, if applicable:

_____

_____

_____

_____

_____

➤ Are the "secret shopper" purchases followed up thoroughly to ensure that the transactions were recorded correctly, not voided, etc.?

Yes   No   N/A

____   ____   ____

If no, explain and record recommendations for improvement, if applicable:

_____

_____

_____

_____

_____

➤ Does the organization use a "secret shopper" for purchases via the mail, websites, etc., with cash, checks, and credit cards?

Yes   No   N/A

____   ____   ____

If no, explain and record recommendations for improvement, if applicable:

_____

_____

_____

_____

_____

➤ Are the "secret shopper" purchases via the mail, websites, etc. followed up thoroughly?

Yes   No   N/A

____   ____   ____

If no, explain and record recommendations for improvement, if applicable:

_____

_____

_____

_____

_____

➤ Are the checks that come into the
organization via the mail and point of
purchase endorsed with the organization's   Yes   No   N/A
restrictive endorsement stamp immediately?   ____   ____   ____

If no, explain and record recommendations for improvement, if applicable:

_____

_____

_____

_____

_____

➤ Does the organization's restrictive
endorsement stamp *not* include the
organization's bank account number?
(Note: Investigate bank requirements   Yes   No   N/A
regarding this policy first.)   ____   ____   ____

If no, explain and record recommendations for improvement, if applicable:

_____

_____

_____

_____

_____

➤ Once checks have been endorsed, are they   Yes   No   N/A
forwarded directly to finance for processing?   ____   ____   ____

If no, explain and record recommendations for improvement, if applicable:

_____

_____

_____

_____

_____

➤ Are nonfinancial employees prohibited
   from receiving original checks after they   Yes   No   N/A
   have been endorsed?   ____   ____   ____

   If no, explain and record recommendations for improvement, if applicable:

_____

_____

_____

_____

_____

➤ Is a log of checks received maintained by
   the person who opens the mail, for audit   Yes   No   N/A
   trail purposes?   ____   ____   ____

   If no, explain and record recommendations for improvement, if applicable:

_____

_____

_____

_____

_____

➤ Are controls protecting private customer
   information regarding credit cards and   Yes   No   N/A
   checks adequate?   ____   ____   ____

   If no, explain and record recommendations for improvement, if applicable:

_____

_____

_____

_____

_____

➤ Does the organization have adequate procedures in place regarding the acceptance of a transaction as an account receivable?

Yes   No   N/A

_____   _____   _____

If no, explain and record recommendations for improvement, if applicable:

_____

_____

_____

_____

_____

➤ Does the organization mail out customer statements on a monthly basis?

Yes   No   N/A

_____   _____   _____

If no, explain and record recommendations for improvement, if applicable:

_____

_____

_____

_____

_____

➤ Does the organization compile an accounts receivable aging schedule monthly?

Yes   No   N/A

_____   _____   _____

If no, explain and record recommendations for improvement, if applicable:

_____

_____

_____

_____

_____

➤ Does the organization have adequate procedures to follow up on aging accounts receivable?

Yes   No   N/A

_____   _____   _____

If no, explain and record recommendations for improvement, if applicable:

_____

_____

_____

_____

_____

➤ Are customer statements reviewed and
controlled by an employee other than the   Yes   No   N/A
accounts receivable clerk?   ____   ____   ____

If no, explain and record recommendations for improvement, if applicable:

_____

_____

_____

_____

_____

➤ Note the organization's procedures for handling delinquent accounts:

_____

_____

_____

_____

_____

➤ Are the procedures concerning following up   Yes   No
on delinquent accounts adequate?   ____   ____

If no, explain and record recommendations for improvement, if applicable:

_____

_____

_____

_____

_____

➤ Note the organization's procedures for writing off uncollectible accounts
receivable:

_____

_____

_____

_____

_____

➤ Are the procedures concerning writing off   Yes   No
uncollectible accounts receivable adequate?   _____   _____

If no, explain and record recommendations for improvement, if applicable:

_____

_____

_____

_____

_____

➤ Note the names and titles of employees authorized to approve accounts receivable write-offs:

Name	Title

➤ Note the names and titles of employees authorized to issue credit memos to customers:

Name	Title

➤ Are procedures surrounding the issuance   Yes   No   N/A
of credit memos adequate?   _____   _____   _____

If no, explain and record recommendations for improvement, if applicable:

_____

_____

_____

_____

_____

➤ If discounts are offered by the organization for prompt payments, describe the procedures:

_____

_____

_____

_____

_____

➤ Is the organization's prompt payment
discount reasonable, and are surrounding   Yes   No   N/A
controls adequate?   ____   ____   ____

If no, explain and record recommendations for improvement, if applicable:

_____

_____

_____

_____

_____

➤ Are the controls concerning offering credit
to customers experiencing a bad debt   Yes   No   N/A
adequate?   ____   ____   ____

If no, explain and record recommendations for improvement, if applicable:

_____

_____

_____

_____

_____

Comment on specific issues concerning recording accounts receivables, securing proper write-off approvals, etc., that indicate controls are not adequate, and record recommendations for improvement:

_____

_____

_____

_____

_____

Disbursements and Accounts Payable

➤ Is the check supply under lock and key?   Yes   No

                                                                ———   ———

If no, explain and record recommendations for improvement, if applicable:

_____

_____

_____

_____

_____

➤ Does the organization utilize a bank's   Yes   No
Positive Pay service?   ———   ———

If yes, explain Positive Pay procedures:

_____

_____

_____

_____

_____

➤ If the organization does not utilize Positive
Pay, have the benefits of this service been
explained to the appropriate level   Yes   No   N/A
of management?   ———   ———   ———

Note details accordingly:

_____

_____

_____

_____

_____

➤ Are individuals involved in the finance
or accounting function prohibited from   Yes   No   N/A
signing checks?   ———   ———   ———

If no, explain and record recommendations for improvement, if applicable:

_____

_____

_____

_____

_____

➤ Does the organization use a purchase   Yes   No   N/A
order system, and are procedures adequate?   ____   ____   ____

If no, explain and record recommendations for improvement, if applicable:

_____

_____

_____

_____

_____

➤ Is the current system of approving invoices   Yes   No
from vendors adequate?   ____   ____

If no, explain and record recommendations for improvement, if applicable:

_____

_____

_____

_____

_____

➤ Are two signatures required on all   Yes   No
disbursements?   ____   ____

If no, explain and record recommendations for improvement, if applicable:

_____

_____

_____

_____

_____

➤ Are there periodic comparisons of
witnessed check-signing signatures   Yes   No
against canceled checks?
                                            ____   ____

If no, explain and record recommendations for improvement, if applicable:

_____

_____

_____

_____

_____

➤ Does the organization have a policy
prohibiting having checks made payable   Yes   No
to acronyms?
                                            ____   ____

If no, explain and record recommendations for improvement, if applicable:

_____

_____

_____

_____

_____

➤ If handwritten or typed checks are ever
prepared, is the amount protected with a   Yes   No   N/A
check imprinter machine?
                                            ____   ____   ____

If no, explain and record recommendations for improvement, if applicable:

_____

_____

_____

_____

_____

➤ If handwritten checks are ever prepared, are
they written with a gel pen rather than an   Yes   No   N/A
ink pen?
                                            ____   ____   ____

If no, explain and record recommendations for improvement, if applicable:

_____

_____

_____

_____

_____

➤ Other than petty cash, are all disbursements   Yes   No
made by check or wire transfer?   ____   ____

If no, explain and record recommendations for improvement, if applicable:

_____

_____

_____

_____

➤ Does the organization prohibit having   Yes   No
checks payable to "cash"?   ____   ____

If no, explain and record recommendations for improvement, if applicable:

_____

_____

_____

_____

➤ Are checks voided properly (cutting off   Yes   No
signature lines)?   ____   ____

If no, explain and record recommendations for improvement, if applicable:

_____

_____

_____

_____

_____

➤ Are voided checks accounted for properly?   Yes   No
                                                      ____   ____

If no, explain and record recommendations for improvement, if applicable:

_____

_____

_____

_____

_____

➤ Does the organization prohibit authorized   Yes   No
   signers from signing checks in advance?   ____   ____

If no, explain and record recommendations for improvement, if applicable:

_____

_____

_____

_____

_____

➤ Does the organization use nonscannable   Yes   No
   check stock?   ____   ____

If no, explain and record recommendations for improvement, if applicable:

_____

_____

_____

_____

_____

➤ Authorized wire transfer agents:

            <u>Name</u>   <u>Title</u>

_____   _____

_____   _____

_____   _____

➤ Are two signatures required on all wire   Yes   No
   transfers?   ____   ____

If no, explain and record recommendations for improvement, if applicable:

_____

_____

_____

_____

_____

➤ Detailed wire transfer procedures:

_____

_____

_____

_____

_____

➤ Does the organization have an accounts
   payable check disbursement policy, and   Yes   No
   has it been communicated to vendors?   ____   ____

If no, explain and record recommendations for improvement, if applicable:

_____

_____

_____

_____

_____

Comment on any specific disbursement issues that indicate that controls are not adequate, with recommendations for improvement:

_____

_____

_____

_____

_____

Inventory

➤ Does the organization capitalize inventory?   Yes   No   N/A

                                                                            ____   ____   ____

If no, explain and record recommendations for improvement, if applicable:

_____

_____

_____

_____

_____

➤ What method of inventory valuation does the organization use? _____

➤ How often are physical inventory counts taken? _____

➤ Is the custodian of inventory separate   Yes   No   N/A
   from purchasing?   ____   ____   ____

If no, explain and record recommendations for improvement, if applicable:

_____

_____

_____

_____

_____

➤ How are discrepancies between physical inventory counts and general ledger balances investigated?

_____

_____

_____

_____

_____

➤ Detail how obsolete inventory is handled, and make recommendations for improvement, if applicable:

_____

_____

_____

_____

_____

➤ Is the year-end inventory verified by an   Yes   No   N/A
   independent party (CPA, etc.)?   ____   ____   ____

   If no, explain and record recommendations for improvement, if applicable:

_____

_____

_____

_____

_____

➤ Are instructions for year-end inventory   Yes   No   N/A
   counts for participating employees adequate?   ____   ____   ____

   If no, explain and record recommendations for improvement, if applicable:

_____

_____

_____

_____

_____

➤ Are consignment inventories adequately   Yes   No   N/A
   segregated from organization inventory?   ____   ____   ____

   If no, explain and record recommendations for improvement, if applicable:

_____

_____

_____

_____

_____

Comment on any inventory issues that indicate improvements are needed, and record recommendations for improvement:

_____

_____

_____

_____

_____

Fixed Assets, Depreciation, and Amortization

➤ What is the organization's capitalization cut-off point? $_____

➤ Does the organization have a capital budget?   Yes   No   N/A

    _____   _____   _____

If no, explain and record recommendations for improvement, if applicable:

_____

_____

_____

_____

➤ Are the purchases of nonbudgeted fixed
  assets approved by the appropriate level   Yes   No   N/A
  of management?

    _____   _____   _____

If no, explain and record recommendations for improvement, if applicable:

_____

_____

_____

_____

_____

➤ What type of depreciation method does the organization use? _____

➤ Does the organization apply fixed asset   Yes   No   N/A
  control numbers to equipment?

    _____   _____   _____

If no, explain and record recommendations for improvement, if applicable:

_____

_____

_____

_____

_____

➤ Are the fixed asset records complete   Yes   No   N/A
  and current?

    _____   _____   _____

If no, explain and record recommendations for improvement, if applicable:

_____

_____

_____

_____

_____

➢ How often are fixed asset records verified against fixed assets on hand?

_____

_____

_____

_____

_____

➢ Describe fixed asset retirement procedures and recommendations for improvement, if applicable:

_____

_____

_____

_____

_____

Comment on any fixed asset procedures that you feel are inadequate, and suggest recommendations for improvement:

_____

_____

_____

_____

_____

Travel Expenses

➤ Does the organization issue travel advances?   Yes   No   N/A

        ____   ____   ____

If yes, describe procedures:

_____

_____

_____

_____

_____

➤ Does the organization require original receipts   Yes   No   N/A
for travel expenses?

        ____   ____   ____

If no, explain and record recommendations for improvement, if applicable:

_____

_____

_____

_____

_____

➤ Are travel expense policies current,   Yes   No   N/A
documented, and communicated properly?

        ____   ____   ____

If no, explain and record recommendations for improvement, if applicable:

_____

_____

_____

_____

_____

➤ Does the organization use the per diem   Yes   No   N/A
method for meal allowances?

        ____   ____   ____

If yes, describe procedures:

_____

_____

_____

_____

_____

➤ Does the organization monitor air fare
rates to ensure that it is benefitting from   Yes   No   N/A
the best available rates?   ____   ____   ____

If no, explain and record recommendations for improvement, if applicable:

_____

_____

_____

_____

_____

➤ Are the organization's travel expense
forms current, complete, and compliant   Yes   No   N/A
with the organization's travel policies?   ____   ____   ____

If no, explain and record recommendations for improvement, if applicable:

_____

_____

_____

_____

_____

Attach current travel approval and reimbursement forms.

Comment on any specific travel issues that indicate that controls and policies are
not adequate, and record recommendations for improvement:

_____

_____

_____

_____

_____

Postage and Shipping

➤ Describe how the organization funds postage in the following areas:

Office postage meter: _____

_____

_____

Business reply mail: _____

_____

_____

Bulk mail: _____

_____

_____

Media mail: _____

_____

_____

Others: _____

_____

_____

➤ Has the organization communicated to
the post office that overages and refunds
will be credited to the organization's postal
account, and that cash refunds are   Yes   No   N/A
not permitted?   ____   ____   ____

If no, explain and record recommendations for improvement, if applicable:

_____

_____

_____

_____

_____

➤ Are policies and controls over access to
postage meters and accounts adequate to   Yes   No   N/A
prevent unauthorized use?   ____   ____   ____

If no, explain and record recommendations for improvement, if applicable:

_____

_____

_____

_____

_____

➤ If the organization uses a shipping service, note the following:

Name of Service _____

Address _____

_____

_____

Contact Name _____

Telephone Number _____

➤ Are the procedures surrounding utilization   Yes   No   N/A
of the organization's mail service adequate?   ____   ____   ____

If no, explain and record recommendations for improvement, if applicable:

_____

_____

_____

_____

Comment on any specific issues that indicate that controls and policies surrounding postal meters, postal accounts, and shipping services are inadequate, and record recommendations for improvement:

_____

_____

_____

_____

_____

Fidelity Bonds

➤ Does the organization have a Fidelity Bond?   Yes   No   N/A

          ____   ____   ____

If no, explain and record recommendations for improvement, if applicable:

_____

_____

_____

_____

_____

➤ If the organization has a Fidelity Bond, note the following:

Insurance Company _____

Address _____

_____

Agent Name _____

Telephone Number _____

Emergency Telephone Number _____

Policy Number _____

Amount of Bond $ _____

Deductible $ _____

➤ Is the amount of the bond adequate?   Yes   No   N/A

          ____   ____   ____

If no, explain and record recommendations for improvement, if applicable:

_____

_____

_____

_____

_____

➤ Are there any Fidelity Bond requirements due
to line of credit agreements, floor plans,   Yes   No   N/A
grants, mortgages, notes, etc.?   ____   ____   ____

If yes, explain and record recommendations for improvement, if applicable:

_____

_____

_____

_____

_____

➤ Are all employees who handle cash,
checks, and credit card transactions   Yes   No   N/A
included in the Fidelity Bond?   ____   ____   ____

If no, explain and record recommendations for improvement, if applicable:

_____

_____

_____

_____

_____

➤ Has it been explained to management that
corporate officers and directors are excluded   Yes   No   N/A
from Fidelity Bond coverage?   ____   ____   ____

Note details accordingly:

_____

_____

_____

_____

_____

Comment on any specific Fidelity Bond issues that indicate that coverage is not
adequate or complete, and note recommendations for improvement:

_____

_____

_____

_____

_____

Gift Offers

➤ Does the organization have a policy
requiring all employees to make the
appropriate level of management aware
that they have been offered gifts by vendors,   Yes   No   N/A
officials, etc.?   _____   _____   _____

If no, explain and record recommendations for improvement, if applicable:

_____

_____

_____

_____

_____

➤ Does the organization require all vendors to
inform the appropriate level of management   Yes   No   N/A
of any intention of offering gifts to employees? _____ _____   _____

If no, explain and record recommendations for improvement, if applicable:

_____

_____

_____

_____

_____

Comment on any specific issues relating to gift offers that indicate that controls are
not adequate, and record recommendations for improvement:

_____

_____

_____

_____

_____

Cash, Cash Equivalents, and Investments

➤ Note all organization checking accounts, money markets, etc.:

Bank Name	Type	Account Number
_____	_____	_____
_____	_____	_____
_____	_____	_____

➤ Note all organization certificates of deposit:

Bank Name	Certificate Number	Interest Rate	Maturity Date
_____	_____	_____	_____
_____	_____	_____	_____
_____	_____	_____	_____

➤ Note all organization investments as follows:

Description (100 Shares of XYZ)	Location (Safe Deposit Box, etc.)
_____	_____
_____	_____
_____	_____
_____	_____

➤ Has the existence of all cash accounts, cash equivalents, and securities been verified?

Yes ____   No ____

If no, explain and record recommendations for improvement, if applicable:

_____

_____

_____

_____

_____

➤ Is the security of investments adequate (safe deposit box, safe, securities, etc.)?

Yes ____   No ____   N/A ____

If no, explain and record recommendations for improvement, if applicable:

_____

_____

_____

_____

_____

➤ Names and titles of employees having access to investments:

Name	Title
_____	_____
_____	_____
_____	_____

➤ Is the log of individuals accessing investments adequate?

Yes   No   N/A
____ ____ ____

If no, explain and record recommendations for improvement, if applicable:

_____

_____

_____

_____

_____

➤ Are investments examined routinely by responsible parties?

Yes   No   N/A
____ ____ ____

If no, explain and record recommendations for improvement, if applicable:

_____

_____

_____

_____

_____

➤ Does the organization have an adequate
investment policy approved by the board   Yes   No   N/A
of directors?
_____   _____   _____

If no, explain and record recommendations for improvement, if applicable:

_____

_____

_____

_____

_____

Comment on any specific cash, cash equivalents, or investment procedures or
issues that indicate that the system and controls are not adequate, with recommendations for improvement:

_____

_____

_____

_____

_____

Implementing an Embezzlement and Fraud Action Plan

➤ Has the CPA firm provided the appropriate level of management with an action plan of steps to take in the event of fraud or embezzlement?

Yes ____   No ____

If no, explain and record recommendations for improvement, if applicable:

_____

_____

_____

_____

_____

➤ Have all employees signed the Conditions of Employment agreement?

Yes ____   No ____   N/A ____

If no, explain and record recommendations for improvement, if applicable:

_____

_____

_____

_____

_____

➤ Have all employees signed the Conflicts of Interest agreement?

Yes ____   No ____   N/A ____

If no, explain and record recommendations for improvement, if applicable:

_____

_____

_____

_____

_____

➤ Emergency Contact Information:

Chief Executive Officer:

    Name _____

    Home Address _____

        _____

    Home Telephone _____

    Cellular Telephone _____

    Business Telephone _____

Treasurer:

    Name _____

    Home Address _____

        _____

    Home Telephone _____

    Cellular Telephone _____

    Business Telephone _____

Chief Financial Officer:

    Name _____

    Home Address _____

        _____

    Home Telephone _____

    Cellular Telephone _____

    Business Telephone _____

Other Staff:

    Name _____

    Home Address _____

        _____

    Home Telephone _____

    Cellular Telephone _____

    Business Telephone _____

CPA Firm:

    Managing Partner Name _____

    Home Address _____

    _____

    Business Telephone _____

    Emergency Telephone _____

    Cellular Telephone _____

    In-Charge Accountant Name _____

    Home Address _____

    _____

    Business Telephone _____

    Emergency Telephone _____

    Cellular Telephone _____

Bank Contacts:

    Bank Officer Name _____

    Branch _____

    Branch Address _____

    _____

    Business Telephone _____

    Emergency Telephone _____

Insurance and Fidelity Bond:

    Insurance Agent Name _____

    Agency _____

    Address _____

    _____

    Business Telephone _____

    Emergency Telephone _____

    Policy Number _____

Attorney:

Name _____

Firm _____

Address _____

_____

Business Telephone _____

Emergency Telephone _____

Cellular Telephone _____

Police Information:

Station Name _____

Station Address _____

_____

Telephone Number to Report Fraud or Embezzlement _____

➤ Have the appropriate levels of management
been advised of the importance of
safeguarding original documents and   Yes   No
working from copies, in the event of fraud?   ____   ____

If no, explain and record recommendations for improvement, if applicable:

_____

_____

_____

_____

_____

➤ Have the appropriate levels of management
been advised of the importance of
taking detailed and copious notes, in the   Yes   No
event of fraud or embezzlement?   ____   ____

If no, explain and record recommendations for improvement, if applicable:

_____

_____

_____

_____

_____

➤ Are the appropriate levels of management
aware of the importance of contacting the
bank(s) immediately in the event of fraud
or embezzlement, in order to have accounts   Yes   No
frozen?   ____   ____

If no, explain and record recommendations for improvement, if applicable:

_____

_____

_____

_____

_____

➤ Does the CPA firm have a predetermined
fraud investigation team familiar with the   Yes   No   N/A
specifics of the organization?   ____   ____   ____

If no, explain and record recommendations for improvement, if applicable:

_____

_____

_____

_____

_____

Comment on any specific embezzlement and fraud action plan issues that indicate
that more study and communication with management are needed:

_____

_____

_____

_____

_____

Note any other internal control issues and recommendations for improvement not addressed in this guide:

_____

_____

_____

_____

_____

_____

_____

_____

_____

_____

_____

_____

_____

_____

_____

_____

_____

_____

_____

_____

_____

_____

_____

_____

_____

Fraud Glossary[1]

Advance Fee Fraud. Falsely obtaining an advance fee for work or services not performed.

Alford **Plea.** Named after the Supreme Court case that upheld the practice under which a defendant pleads guilty, although continuing to assert innocence. Such a plea may be made to obtain the benefits of a plea agreement and to avoid potentially more dire consequences, such as the death penalty, if the defendant is convicted after trial.

Anti-Kickback Act of 1986. The provisions of this act are contained in Title 41, U.S. Code §§ 51–58. The act outlaws the giving or receiving of anything of value for the purpose of improperly obtaining or receiving favorable treatment in connection with U.S. government contracts.

Arbitration. Process whereby the dispute is submitted to an impartial third person who then decides the outcome of the case, that is, which party should win. The arbitrator acts as a judge or jury would, by deciding the case on its merits. An arbitration can be either "binding" or "nonbinding." If the arbitration is binding, then the decision of the arbitrator is final, and the parties cannot later submit their dispute to a judge or jury for determination.

Arraignment. Because of due process considerations, the defendant has to be brought before the court shortly after his arrest. He enters a plea at this time, in a

---

1 © 1999 Association of Certified Fraud Examiners. Major portions of this Glossary reprinted with permission.

proceeding that is called an *arraignment*. He will be given notice of the charges against him, be informed of his rights, and, if applicable, bail will be set.

Attorney Work Product Doctrine.   Under Rule 26(b)(3) of the Federal Rules of Civil Procedure, documents and tangible things that are prepared in anticipation of litigation or for a trial are protected by the work product privilege. The information may be disclosed only if the opposing party can show "substantial need" for the protected information and show that the information cannot be obtained from another source. The privilege extends to information prepared by or for a party or the party's representative, including attorneys and consultants.

Attorney-Client Privilege.   This privilege precludes disclosure of communications between an attorney and client, but only if the following conditions are met: (1) the client retained the attorney, (2) to provide legal advice, (3) and thereafter communicated with the attorney on a confidential basis, and, (4) has not waived the privilege.

Audit Exceptions.   Problems incurred during the course of an audit by the independent CPA or the IRS.

Best Evidence **Rule.**   Prohibits a party from testifying about the contents of a document without producing the document itself. Also known as the *original writing rule*, it requires that when a witness testifies about the contents of a document, at least a fair copy of the original must be available for inspection. If there isn't an original, an authenticatible copy will do.

Bid-Rigging Schemes.   The acceptance or payment of bribes or kickbacks in construction contracts. Bid-rigging schemes can be categorized based on the stage of bidding at which the fraudster exerts his influence. Bid-rigging schemes usually occur in the presolicitation phase, the solicitation phase, or the submission phase of the bidding process.

Billing Schemes.   Type of asset misappropriation scheme that allows the perpetrator to misappropriate company funds without ever actually handling cash or checks while at work. There are three principal types of billing schemes: false invoicing via shell companies, false invoicing via nonaccomplice vendors, and personal purchases made with company funds.

Biological Theories.   Biological theories maintain that criminal behavior is not the result of choice, that is, the calculation of benefits and potential losses, but rather is caused by the physical traits of those who commit crime.

Brady **Material.** Exculpatory information possessed by the government. Refers to the 1963 decision by the U.S. Supreme Court in *Brady v. Maryland*, 373 U.S. 83. Under *Brady*, the prosecution must disclose all evidence requested by the defendant that is material to guilt or punishment, that is, evidence that would tend to *exculpate* him or reduce his penalty. The government is expressly forbidden to conceal evidence that would call the charges into question.

Bribery. Includes official bribery, which refers to the corruption of a public official, and commercial bribery, which refers to the corruption of a private individual to gain a commercial or business advantage. The elements of official bribery vary by jurisdiction, but generally are: (1) giving or receiving, (2) a thing of value, (3) to influence, (4) an official act.

Bustout. A planned bankruptcy. It can take many different forms. The basic approach is for an apparently legitimate business to order large quantities of goods on credit, then dispose of those goods through legitimate or illegitimate channels. The perpetrators then close shop, absconding with the proceeds, and leaving the suppliers unpaid.

Cash Larceny. The intentional taking away of an employer's cash (the term "cash" includes both currency and checks) without the consent and against the will of the employer.

Chain of Custody. Refers to (1) who has had possession of an object, and (2) what they've done with it. The chain of custody must be preserved, or else the item cannot be used at trial.

Check Tampering. Type of fraudulent disbursement scheme in which the perpetrator physically prepares the fraudulent check. Usually, the perpetrator takes physical control of a check and makes it payable to himself through one of several methods. Most check-tampering crimes fall into one of four categories: forged maker schemes, intercepted check schemes, concealed check schemes, and authorized maker schemes.

Chronemic Communication. Refers to the use of time in interpersonal relationships to convey meaning, attitudes, and desires. If the respondent is late in keeping an appointment, for example, this might convey a lack of interest in or avoidance of the interview.

Churning.   Churning occurs when agents falsely tell customers that they can buy additional insurance for nothing by using built-up value in their current policies. In reality, the cost of the new policies frequently exceeds the value of the old ones.

Circumstantial Evidence.   Evidence that tends to prove or disprove facts in issue indirectly, by inference. Many fraud cases are proved entirely by circumstantial evidence, or by a combination of circumstantial and direct evidence, but seldom by direct evidence alone. The most difficult element to prove in many fraud cases—fraudulent intent—is usually proved circumstantially, and necessarily so, because direct proof of the defendant's state of mind, absent a confession or the testimony of a co-conspirator, is impossible.

Civil Monetary Penalty Law (CMPL).   The Civil Monetary Penalty Law (42 U.S. Code § 1320a-7a) was passed to impose administrative sanctions against providers who defraud any federally funded program by filing false claims by other improper billing practices. Any person (including an organization, agency, or other entity, but excluding a beneficiary) that presents or causes to be presented a claim for a medical or other item or service, when the person knows or should know the claim is false or fraudulent, is subject to a civil monetary penalty.

Common Law.   Consists of the usages and customs of a society as interpreted by the judiciary; it often is referred to as "judge-made" law.

Compensating Controls.   When adequate internal controls are precluded due to very small staffs or other factors, other controls are implemented.

Computer Crime.   Illegal act either conducted against the computer (such as data alteration) or in which the computer is an integral part of the improper act.

Computer Fraud.   Any defalcation or embezzlement accomplished by tampering with computer programs, data files, operations, equipment, or media, and resulting in losses sustained by the organization whose computer system was manipulated. The distinguishing characteristic of computer fraud is that access occurs with the intent to execute a fraudulent scheme.

Computer Fraud and Abuse Act.   A statute enacted in 1984, Title 18 U.S. Code, Section 1030, makes certain computer-related activity a specific federal offense. In brief, Section 1030 punishes any intentional, unauthorized access to a "protected computer" for the purpose of: obtaining restricted data regarding national security, obtaining confidential financial information, using a computer that is intended for use by the U.S. government, committing a fraud, or damaging or destroying information contained in the computer.

Computer Hacking.   Prior to newspapers using the term *hacker* to describe a computer criminal, the term was used to define a computer enthusiast. The term is now associated with unauthorized computer activity. Hacking or "phreaking" is basically the breaking into computers and telecommunications systems by learning the vulnerabilities of various types of hardware and software, and using a computer to systematically "guess" the telephone number, user's system identification, and password.

Computer Viruses.   A computer virus is a program that contains instruction code to attack software. Some viruses are hidden computer programs that use all the computer's resources thereby shutting down the system or slowing it down significantly. Computer viruses range from the relatively harmless (displaying a message or greeting) to shutdowns of entire computer networks for extended periods.

Computer-Assisted Crime.   Use of computers instead of other means to break the law.

Conflict of Interest.   Occurs when an employee, manager, or executive has an undisclosed economic or personal interest in a transaction, which adversely affects that person's employer. As with other corruption frauds, conflict schemes involve the exertion of an employee's influence to the detriment of his company. In bribery schemes, fraudsters are paid to exercise their influence on behalf of a third party, whereas conflict cases involve self-dealing by an employee.

Corporate Fraud.   Corporate fraud is any fraud perpetrated by, for, or against a business corporation. Corporate frauds can be internally generated (perpetrated by agents, employees, and executives of a corporation, for or against it, or against others) or externally generated (by others against the corporation, that is suppliers, vendors, customers).

COSO Report.   The Committee of Sponsoring Organizations (COSO) was formed to support the implementation of the Treadway Commission findings. In 1992 the committee issued *Internal Control—Integrated Framework*. This report was a collaborative effort of the American Accounting Association, the American Institute of CPAs, the Financial Executives Institute, the Institute of Internal Auditors, and the Institute of Management Accountants.

Counterclaim.   A claim field by a defendant against the plaintiff in a civil suit. Popularly known as a "countersuit."

Criteria-Based Statement Analysis.   Analyzing the language used by the subject to assess its truthfulness.

Cross-Claim.   An action or claim between co-parties, that is, claims between two defendants or two plaintiffs.

Defalcation.   The act of a defaulter; act of embezzling; failure to meet an obligation; misappropriation of trust funds or money held in any fiduciary capacity; failure to properly account for such funds. Commonly applied to officers of corporations or public officials (*Black's Law Dictionary*, 1990).

Defamation.   The four elements of defamation are (1) a false statement of fact, (2) tending to subject the person to whom it referred to ill will or disrepute, (3) published to one or more persons, and (4) made without privilege.

Defense.   An assertion by a defendant in a criminal or civil suit that seeks to explain away guilt or civil liability for damages.

Demonstrative Evidence.   A tangible item that illustrates some material proposition (e.g., a map, a chart, a summary). It differs from real evidence in that demonstrative evidence was not part of the underlying event; it was created specifically for the trial. Its purpose is to provide a visual aid for the jury.

Deposition.   Sworn testimony given by a party or witness upon questioning by counsel for one of the parties before trial and outside of court, usually in a lawyer's office.

Diagnosis-Related Grouping (DRG).   A patient classification scheme that categorizes patients who are medically related with respect to primary and secondary diagnosis, age, and complications.

Direct Evidence.   Includes testimony or other evidence that tends to prove or disprove a fact in issue directly, such as eyewitness testimony or a confession. See also *Circumstantial Evidence*.

Discovery.   The formal process whereby the parties collect evidence and learn the details of the opposing case. Under federal rules, either party may take discovery regarding any matter, not privileged, that is relevant to the subject matter of the action, or that might lead to admissible evidence. The principal means of discovery are oral depositions, written interrogatories, and requests to produce documents.

Duty of Care.   The duty of a corporate officer, director, or high-level employee, as well as other people in a fiduciary relationship, to conduct business affairs prudently with the skill and attention normally exercised by people in similar positions.

Duty of Loyalty.   Requires that an employee/agent act solely in the best interest of the employer/principal, free of any self-dealing, conflicts of interest, or other abuse of the principal for personal advantage.

Duty of Obedience.   A standard requiring all members of the board of directors, officers, trustees, and key employees to follow federal and state laws as well as their organization's bylaws.

Economic Extortion.   Economic extortion cases are "Pay up or else. . ." corruption schemes—basically the flip side of bribery schemes. Instead of a vendor offering a payment to influence a decision, an employee demands that a vendor pay him to make a decision in that vendor's favor. If the vendor refuses to pay, he faces some harm such as a loss of business with the extorter's company.

Electronic Data Interchange.   Electronic Data Interchange (EDI) is the exchange of electronic data between computers, in which there is no human interaction.

Electronic Funds Transfer (EFT).   An electronic funds transfer (EFT) system is a network of operations designed to move instantaneously funds (e.g., deposits in savings and checking accounts and funds obtained through overdraft and credit arrangements) from one account or institution to another (*Bank Administration Manual*, Bank Administration Institute).

Embezzlement.   The wrongful appropriation of money or property by a person to whom it has been lawfully entrusted. Embezzlement implicitly involves a breach of trust, although it is not necessary to show a fiduciary relationship between the parties.

Employee Polygraph Protection Act.   Prohibits the use of polygraphs by most private employers unless the employer is engaged in an ongoing investigation involving economic loss or injury to the employer in the employer's business and has a reasonable suspicion that the employee is involved in the incident.

Encryption.   An encryption system consists of a cryptographic function, which scrambles an electronic transmission, and an inverse decrypt function, which restores the transmission to its original state. Encryption hardware and software can be used to scramble any communication by utilizing a complex mathematical formula. The only way to unscramble an encrypted message is to provide the unique answer "key," thus unlocking the message.

Evidence.   Anything perceivable by the five senses, and any proof such as testimony of witnesses, records, documents, facts, data, or tangible objects legally presented at trial to prove a contention and induce a belief in the minds of a jury.

Exclusionary Rule.   This rule commands that where evidence has been obtained in violation of the search and seizure protections guaranteed by the U.S. Constitution, the illegally obtained evidence cannot be used at the trial of the defendant. Under this rule, evidence that is obtained by an unreasonable search and seizure is excluded from admissibility under the Fourth Amendment, and this rule has been held to be applicable to the States. "Good faith exception" to the exclusionary rule provides that evidence is not to be suppressed under such rule where that evidence was discovered by officers acting in good faith and in reasonable, though mistaken, belief that they were authorized to take those actions. (*Black's Law Dictionary*, 1990.)

Expert Witness.   One who by reason of education or specialized experience possesses superior knowledge respecting a subject about which persons having no particular training are incapable of forming an accurate opinion or deducting a correct conclusion (*Kim Mfg., Inc. v. Superior Metal Treating, Inc.*, Mo. App., 537 S. W.2d 424, 428).

External Fraud Schemes.   Fraud schemes that are committed by outside organizations, typically by individuals or groups of individuals, against organizations.

Extortion.   The obtaining of property from another, with the other party's "consent" having been induced by wrongful use of actual or threatened force or fear. Fear might include the apprehension of possible economic damage or loss. A demand for a bribe or kickback also might constitute extortion.

Fair Credit Reporting Act.   One of the primary statutes limiting the access to personal information is the federal Fair Credit Reporting Act (FCRA). This statute regulates the dissemination of consumer information to third parties by consumer reporting agencies. It prohibits the disclosure of any consumer credit report (the terms are defined in the statute) except in accordance with the Act. Its purpose is to regulate the activities and record keeping of mercantile credit, insurance, and employment investigation agencies and bureaus.

False Claims and Statements. Chapter 47 of Title 18, U.S. Code, contains a number of related provisions that punish false or fraudulent statements, oral or written, made to various federal agencies and departments. The principal statute is Section 1001, which prohibits such statements generally and overlaps with many of the more specific laws, such as Section 1014, that apply to false statements made on certain loan and credit applications.

False Imprisonment. Restraint by one person of the physical liberty of another without consent or legal justification.

False Pretenses. Illegally obtaining money, goods, or merchandise from another by fraud or misrepresentation. As a statutory crime, although defined in slightly different ways in the various jurisdictions, it consists generally of these elements: (1) an intent to defraud, (2) the use of false pretenses or representations regarding any existing facts, and (3) the accomplishment of the intended fraud by means of such false pretenses (*People v. Johnson*, 28 Mich. App. 10, 183 N.W.2d 813, 815, 816).

Fidelity Bond. A policy issued by many large insurance companies under which the insured entity is covered against losses caused by the dishonest or fraudulent acts of its employees.

Financial Statement Fraud. Fraud committed to falsify financial statements, usually committed by management, and normally involving overstating income or assets or understating liabilities or expenses.

Firewalls. Firewalls are advanced software programs that effectively "lock up" access to an Internet site or email transmission. Firewalls are designed to control the interface between a network and the Internet. This technology surveys incoming and outgoing transmissions between the network and the Internet, stopping any questionable transmission attempt to access a sensitive area.

Foreign Corrupt Practices Act. The provisions of the FCPA are found in Title 15, U.S. Code, §78m. The FCPA amended the 1934 Act to prohibit certain publicly held companies from making corrupt payments to foreign officials or political organizations. Other amendments to the Act make it illegal for any U.S. citizen to make such payments.

Forensic.   Of or relating to the courts.

Fraud.   Any intentional or deliberate act to deprive another of property or money by guile, deception, or other unfair means.

Fraud Examination.   A methodology for resolving fraud allegations from inception to disposition. More specifically, fraud examination involves obtaining evidence and taking statements, writing reports, testifying to findings, and assisting in the detection and prevention of fraud.

Fraud Theory Approach.   The fraud theory approach begins with the assumption, based on the known facts, of what might have occurred. Then that assumption is tested to determine whether it is provable. The fraud theory approach involves the following steps, in the order of their occurrence: (1) analyze available data, (2) create a hypothesis, (3) test the hypothesis, (4) refine and amend the hypothesis.

Fraudulent Disbursement Schemes.   Type of occupational fraud whereby an employee makes a distribution of company funds for a dishonest purpose. Examples of fraudulent disbursements include forging company checks, the submission of false invoices, doctoring timecards, and so forth.

Generally Accepted Accounting Principles (GAAP).   A technical term encompassing conventions, rules, and procedures governing acceptable accounting practice.

Generally Accepted Auditing Standards (GAAS).   Assumptions and rules that govern the CPA's ability to accept an auditing engagement and procedures that must be undertaken during the course of an audit.

Ghost Employee.   Refers to someone on the payroll who does not actually work for the victim company. Through the falsification of personnel or payroll records, a fraudster causes paychecks to be generated to a ghost. The fraudster or an accomplice then converts these paychecks. The ghost employee may be a fictitious person or a real individual who simply does not work for the victim employer. When the ghost is a real person, it is often a friend or relative of the perpetrator.

Ghost Vendor.   A process of billing an organization for goods or services that were never provided, by a vendor that does not exist. Usually perpetrated by someone with authority to approve invoices for payment.

Grand Jury. Consists of 16 to 23 people sworn as jurors who meet in secret deliberation, usually in biweekly or monthly sessions, to hear witnesses and other evidence presented by prosecutors and to vote on indictments. An indictment or *true bill* must be concurred in by at least 12 jurors voting without the prosecutor present.

Horizontal Analysis. A technique for analyzing the percentage change in individual financial statement items from one year to the next. The first period in the analysis is considered the base, and the changes to subsequent periods are computed as a percentage of the base period.

Illegal Gratuities. Similar to bribery schemes, except that there is not necessarily an intent to influence a particular business decision before the fact. In the typical illegal gratuities scenario, a decision is made that happens to benefit a certain person or company. The party who benefitted from the decision then gives a gift to the person who made the decision. The gift could be anything of value. An illegal gratuity does not require proof of intent to influence.

Indictment. In the federal system, all offenses punishable by death must be charged by indictment; all felonies (generally crimes punishable by imprisonment for a year or more) must be prosecuted by indictment, unless the defendant waives the requirement, in which case the prosecution may proceed by the filing of an "Information."

Information. A charge signed only by the prosecutor, without the involvement of the grand jury. See also *Indictment*.

Insider Trading. Consists of using nonpublic information relating to market securities trades.

Interrogatories. Questions that are submitted to an opposing party in a lawsuit. Interrogatories cannot be given to anyone other than a party to a suit. Questions are submitted to the witness in writing. If no objection is given, then the party must answer the questions in writing. All answers must be sworn to under oath.

Interview. A question-and-answer session designed to elicit information. It differs from an ordinary conversation in that the interview is structured, not free-form, and is designed for a purpose. An interview might consist of only one question or a series of questions.

Jencks Act. The Jencks Act, 18 U.S. Code §3500, permits the defendant to obtain, prior to cross-examination, a government witness's prior statements (or portions thereof) that relate to the subject matter of his testimony on direct examination. However, the statute also protects statements from discovery until after the direct examination has been completed.

Jurisdiction. Authority of a court to hear a particular type of case. A probate court, for instance, only has jurisdiction to hear cases related to wills and other probate matters. Lower trial courts (such as a justice of the peace court) may only have jurisdiction to hear matters under a certain dollar amount, for instance, cases with less than $5,000 in controversy.

Kickbacks. In the commercial sense, refers to giving or receiving anything of value to influence a business decision without the employer's knowledge and consent.

Kinesic Interview. Type of interview methodology that is different from traditional interview methods, because the interviewer is not necessarily looking for a confession from the interview subject. Instead of searching for information from the subject, the interviewer is attempting to assess whether the subject is telling the truth. In the book *The Kinesic Interview Technique*, authors Frederick C. Link and D. Glen Foster define the kinesic interview technique as "[An interview technique] used for gaining information from an individual who is not willingly or intentionally disclosing it."

Kinetic Communication. Involves the use of body movement to convey meaning. For example, a person who feels shame normally will drop the eyes to avoid the glance of another. This is not only to avoid seeing disapproval, but to conceal personal shame and confusion.

Kiting. The wrongful practice of taking advantage of the float, the time that elapses between the deposit of a check in one bank and its collection at another. The drawer uses funds that are not his by drawing checks against deposits that have not yet cleared through the banks. Kiting consists of writing checks against a bank account where funds are insufficient to cover them, hoping that before they are presented, the necessary funds will be deposited (*Black's Law Dictionary*, 1990).

Land Flip. Practice of buying and selling real estate very quickly, often several times a day, or at least within a few months. With each sale the price is increased. The sales often are transacted between related parties or with shell corporations.

Their sole purpose is to increase the selling price. Ultimately, the price becomes insupportable.

Larceny.   The wrongful taking of money or property of another with the intent to convert it or to deprive the owner of its possession and use. The transaction has already been recorded and is "on the books."

Libel.   Form of defamation whereby the offending material is communicated by writing or pictures, as opposed to purely oral means.

Management Letter.   Written communication from the auditing CPA firm to the client, detailing material issues that have come to the attention of the auditor during the course of the audit. The Management Letter is not included with audited financial statements and is not limited to internal control issues.

Mail Fraud.   The federal mail fraud statute is Title 18, U.S. Code, §1341. The gist of the offense is the use of the mails as an integral part of a scheme to defraud. The mailing itself does not need to contain the false and fraudulent representations, as long as it is an integral part of the scheme. What is integral or incidental depends on the facts of each case; generally, a mailing that helps advance the scheme in any significant way will be considered sufficient.

Material Weakness.   Weaknesses in internal control that would probably not be detected by auditors, internal auditors, or employees in a timely manner.

Mediation.   Process whereby an impartial third person assists the parties in reaching a resolution of the dispute. The mediator does not decide who should win, but instead works with the parties to reach a mutually agreeable settlement.

***Miranda* Rights.**   Refers to the Supreme Court ruling in the landmark case of *Miranda v. Arizona*, 348 U.S. 436 (1966), that the police must give the following warnings before interrogating any suspect held in custody: (1) the suspect has the right to remain silent, (2) any statements can be used against him at trial, (3) the suspect has a right to the assistance of an attorney, and (4) an attorney will be appointed to represent the suspect if he cannot afford to retain one.

Misapplication.   Wrongful taking or conversion of another's property for the benefit of someone else.

Misappropriation.   The unauthorized, improper, or unlawful use of funds or other property for a purpose other than that for which it was intended.

Misrepresentation of Material Facts. The deliberate making of false statements to induce the intended victim to part with money or property. The elements normally include: (1) a material false statement, (2) knowledge of its falsity, (3) reliance on the false statement by the victim, and (4) damages suffered.

Money Laundering. The disguising of the existence, nature, source, ownership, location, and disposition of property derived from criminal activity. The "washing" of money includes all forms of illegal activities. In most instances, the goal is to conduct transactions in cash (currency) in such a way as to conceal the true nature of transactions.

Multilevel Marketing (MLM). Use of individual sellers and a graduated payment scale to move products. Illegal MLMs use the product as a front while basing their return on new people recruited into the plan.

Net Worth. The amount by which assets exceed liabilities.

Noncompetition Agreement. An agreement whereby an employee agrees not to work for competing companies within a certain period of time after leaving a company.

Nondisclosure Agreement. A written agreement that provides that all proprietary, confidential, or trade secret information learned by the party in the course of business dealings must be kept confidential and must not be disclosed to any third parties.

Norming. Sometimes referred to as "calibrating," norming is the process of observing behavior before critical questions are asked, as opposed to doing so during questioning. People with truthful attitudes will answer questions one way; those with untruthful attitudes generally will answer them differently.

Occupational Fraud and Abuse. The use of one's occupation for personal enrichment through the deliberate misuse or misapplication of the employing organization's resources or assets. Simply stated, occupational frauds are those in which an employee, manager, officer, or owner of an organization commits fraud to the detriment of that organization. The three major types of occupational fraud are: corruption, asset misappropriation, and fraudulent statements (which include financial statement schemes).

Off-Book Fraud.   Involves vendor and vendor employees engaging in bribes, scams, kickbacks, conflicts of interest, bribery, and corruption. Detected by means of tips or complaints from sources either inside or outside the company.

On-Book Fraud.   Involves employees manipulating accounting records. Detected by means of basic audit tests in high-risk areas, using original source documents.

Oversight Committee.   An oversight committee should be established to review uniformity in decision making. Further, it should act as a tribunal for the presentation of additional information *to change* or assist management in making appropriate decisions regarding fraud investigations.

Paralinguistic Communication.   Involves the use of volume, pitch, and voice quality to convey meaning. One of the basic differences between written and verbal communication is that oral speech gives the full range of nonverbal accompaniment. For example, a "no" answer might not really mean no; it depends on the way in which the "no" is said.

Parole Evidence.   Oral or verbal evidence; that which is given by word of mouth, the ordinary kind of evidence given by witnesses in court (*Black's Law Dictionary*, 1990).

Parole Evidence Rule.   This evidence rule seeks to preserve the integrity of written agreements by refusing to permit contracting parties to attempt to alter the import of their contract through use of contemporaneous oral declarations (*Black's Law Dictionary*, 1990).

Phishing.   An email scheme whereby a fraudster poses as a legitimate enterprise to gather financial information such as credit card and bank account numbers from an unknowing victim.

Ponzi Scheme.   The term *Ponzi* refers to illegal operations that use financial instruments of some sort to extract money from victims; there are few or no actual investments being made, just funds passing up a ladder.

Privacy Act of 1974.   Restricts information about individuals, both employees and nonemployees, that might be gathered by *government agencies*. This information might include a person's education, finances, medical history, criminal history, employment history, and identifying information (fingerprint, voice print, or photograph). The employee might have access to the information unless it is investigatory material compiled for law enforcement purposes, statistical records, or material compiled solely for determining suitability, eligibility, or qualification for federal service or promotion.

Probable Cause.   Reasonable cause; having more evidence for than against. A reasonable ground for belief in certain alleged facts. A set of probabilities that is grounded in the factual and practical considerations that govern the decisions of reasonable and prudent persons and is more than mere suspicion but less than the quantum of evidence required for conviction (*Black's Law Dictionary*, 1990).

Proxemic Communication.   Use of interpersonal space to convey meaning. The relationship between the interviewer and respondent is both a cause and effect of proxemic behavior. If the distance between the interviewer and the respondent is greater, there is more of a tendency for them to watch each other's eyes for clues to meaning.

Psychological Theories.   Refers to theories of behavior rooted in psychology and based on the view that criminal behavior is the product of mental processes.

Pyramid Scheme.   A scheme in which a buyer or participant is promised a payment for each additional buyer or participant recruited by that person.

Qui Tam Suit.   A *qui tam* suit is one in which a private individual sues on behalf of the government to recover damages for criminal or fraudulent actions committed against the government. It is a civil, not a criminal, suit. Most qui tam actions are brought under the False Claims Act, 31 U. S. Code §3729 et seq.

Racketeer Influenced and Corrupt Organizations Act (RICO).   Title 18, U.S. Code, §1961, et. seq. The statute outlaws the investment of ill-gotten gains in another business enterprise, the acquisition of an interest in an enterprise through certain illegal acts, and the conduct of the affairs of an enterprise through such acts. Criminal penalties include stiff fines and prison terms, as well as the forfeiture of all illegal proceeds or interests. Civil remedies include treble damages, attorney fees, dissolution of the offending enterprise, and other penalties.

Ratio Analysis.   A means of measuring the relationship between two different financial statement amounts. The relationship and comparison are the keys to the analysis.

Real Evidence.   Refers to physical objects that may be introduced as evidence at a legal proceeding. A canceled check, an invoice, a ledger, letters, and documents are real evidence, but the term includes any physical evidence.

Relevant Evidence.   Rule 401 of the Federal Rules of Evidence defines *relevant evidence* as evidence "having any tendency to make the existence of any fact that is of consequence to determination of the action more probable or less probable than it would be without the evidence." In other words, relevant evidence is evidence that tends to prove or disprove a fact in issue.

Reportable Condition.   A significant deficiency in internal controls that could lead to fraud if not corrected.

Routine Activities Theory.   A variation of classical theory, this theory holds that both the motivation to commit crime and the supply of offenders are constant. There always will be a certain number of people motivated by greed, lust, and other forces inclining toward lawbreaking.

Search Warrants.   Issued by a judge upon presentation of probable cause to believe that records or other items are being used or have been used in the commission of a crime. An affidavit usually is used to support the request for the search warrant. The affidavit must describe in detail the reason(s) the warrant is requested, along with the place the evidence is thought to be kept. Courts cannot issue search warrants without sufficient cause; the Fourth Amendment to the Constitution protects individuals against unreasonable searches and seizures.

Sentencing Guidelines.   The Sentencing Reform Act of 1984 provided for the development of guidelines for the sentencing of individual and organizational offenders. The individual guidelines became effective in 1987, and the guidelines for organizations in 1991.

Shell Companies.   Fictitious business entities created for the sole purpose of committing fraud. They may be nothing more than a fabricated name and a post office box that an employee uses to collect disbursements from false billings.

Skimming.   Removal of cash from a victim entity prior to its entry in an accounting system. Employees who skim from their companies steal sales or receivables before they are recorded in the company books. Skimming schemes are known as "off-book" frauds, meaning money is stolen before it is recorded in the victim organization's accounts.

Slander. Form of defamation whereby a person, persons, or organization is offended by oral rather than written means.

Sliding. "Sliding" is the term used for including additional coverages in the insurance policy without the knowledge of the insured. The extra charges are hidden in the total premium, and because the insured is unaware of the coverage, few claims are ever filed. For example, motor club memberships, accidental death, and travel accident coverages can usually be slipped into the policy without the knowledge of the insured.

Social Control Theory. Travis Hirschi, in his 1969 book, *Causes of Delinquency*, first articulated the *social control theory*. Essentially, control theory argues that the institutions of the social system train and press those with whom they are in contact into patterns of conformity. The theory rests on the thesis that to the extent a person fails to become attached to the variety of control agencies of the society, his/her chances of violating the law are increased.

Social Learning Theories. These theories hold that criminal behavior is a function of the way people absorb information, viewpoints, and motivations from others, most notably from those to whom they are close, such as members of their peer group. Social learning theorists believe that all people have the potential to commit crime if they are exposed to certain kinds of circumstances.

Social Process Theories. These theories hold that criminality is a function of individual socialization and the social-psychological interactions people have with the various organizations, institutions, and processes of society. Although they differ in many respects, the various social process theories all share one basic concept: All people regardless of their race, class, or gender, have the potential to become delinquents or criminals.

Social Structure Theories. Theories of criminology that concentrate on the kinds of societies that generate particular levels of crime. For example, why is crime so low in Japan and so high in the United States? Such theorists argue that people living in equivalent social environments seem to behave in a similar, predictable fashion.

Subpoena Duces Tecum. A legal order requiring the production of documents.

Suspicious Activity Reports. Effective April 1, 1996, the Office of the Comptroller of the Currency (OCC) requires national banks to submit a Suspicious Activity Report (SAR) under certain circumstances (12 C.F.R. §21.11, as amended). Reports are required if there is a known or suspected criminal violation committed against the bank or involving a transaction conducted through the bank.

Tax Fraud. "the actual intentional wrongdoing, and the intent required . . . to evade a tax believed to be owing." Fraud implies bad faith, intentional wrongdoing, and a sinister motive. It is never imputed or presumed and the courts will not sustain findings of fraud upon circumstances which at most create only suspicion. See 14 Mertens, *Law of Federal Income Taxation*, sec. 55.21, page 64 (1991 Rev); *Ross Glove Co. v. Commissioner*, 60 TC 569 (1973).

Telemarketing Fraud. Used to refer to fraud schemes that are perpetrated over the telephone; they most often consist of calls by the telemarketer to the victim to deceive the victim into purchasing goods or services.

Trade Secret. Includes secret formulas and processes, but also any other proprietary information, such as customer and price lists, sales figures, business plans, or any other confidential information that has a value to the business and would be potentially harmful if disclosed.

Treadway Commission. The National Commission on Fraudulent Financial Reporting (commonly known as the Treadway Commission) was established in 1987 with the purpose of defining the responsibility of the auditor in preventing and detecting fraud. The commission was formed by the major professional auditing organizations: the American Institute of Certified Public Accountants, the Institute of Internal Auditors, and the National Association of Accountants.

Trespass. The unauthorized, intentional, or negligent entry upon the property of others. A claim of trespass might arise from a search of an employee's locker. It is particularly applicable to surveillance at an employee's home.

Twisting. Twisting is the replacement, usually by high-pressure sales techniques, of existing policies for new ones. The primary reason, of course, is for the agent to profit, because first-year sales commissions are much higher than commissions for existing policies.

Uniform Commercial Code Filings. In order to obtain a perfected security interest in personal property, a lender must file a Uniform Commercial Code (UCC) statement with the secretary of state or the county. Banks, finance companies, and other lenders will generate records or recorded filings of financial transactions conducted with individuals and businesses, such as purchases of household furniture, appliances, boats and yachts, automobiles, aircraft, and business equipment.

Uniform Crime Reports.   The Federal Bureau of Investigation (FBI) compiles statistics on the extent of crime in the United States in a document called the *Uniform Crime Report* (UCR). The report is put together on the basis of information voluntarily submitted by more than 15,000 law enforcement departments. This includes virtually every significant public policing agency in the country.

Venue.   The geographical area covered by the court. A trial court in Dallas County, Texas, for example, can only hear cases that have some connection with either parties or events that occurred in that county. Venue is technically an element of the court's jurisdiction.

Vertical Analysis.   A technique for analyzing the relationships between the items on an income statement, balance sheet, or statement of cash flows by expressing components as percentages.

Whistleblowers.   Employees who report illegal or unethical conduct of their employers. Federal law and many state laws provide, in some instances, protection to employees who report improper or illegal acts to government authorities. Most of these laws protect the employee from any adverse employment action or retaliatory action from the employer.

Wire Fraud.   The federal wire fraud statute is Title 18, U.S. Code, § 1343. It prohibits transmission "by means of wire, radio, or television communication in interstate or foreign commerce, any writings, signs, signals, pictures, or sounds for the purpose of executing such scheme or artifice." The wire fraud statute often is used in tandem with mail fraud counts in federal prosecutions. Unlike mail fraud, however, wire fraud requires an interstate or foreign communication for a violation.

Yellow Book Standards.   Standards for audits of government organizations, programs, activities, and functions, and of government assistance received by contractors, nonprofit organizations, and other nongovernment organizations, developed by the Comptroller General of the United States, General Accounting Office (GAO). These standards are by and large taken from Generally Accepted Accounting Principles. However, *Government Auditing Standards*, also known as the *Yellow Book*, goes beyond the AICPA standards. Generally Accepted Government Auditing Standards (GAGAS) are to be followed by auditors and audit organizations when required by law, regulation, agreement, contract, or policy.

Index